HOW TO CAST

HOW TO CAST A NATAL CHART

by

JEFF MAYO, *D.M.S.Astrol.(Hon.)*, *D.F.Astrol.S.*
(Principal, The Mayo School of Astrology)
(Principal, Faculty of Astrological Studies, 1969–73)
(Head Tutor, Faculty of Astrological Studies, 1957–73)

Author of *Teach Yourself Astrology*
How to Cast a Natal Chart
How to Read the Ephemeris
The Planets and Human Behaviour

Illustrations by the Author

The Astrologer's Handbook Series No. 3

L. N. FOWLER & CO. LTD.
1201/1203 **HIGH ROAD**
CHADWELL HEATH
ROMFORD RM6 4DH
ESSEX

First Edition 1967
Second Edition March 1970
Third Edition July 1973
Fourth Revised Edition October 1976
Fifth Edition January 1979
Sixth Edition December 1983

8524 3056 6

Printed and bound in Great Britain at
The Camelot Press Ltd, Southampton

Contents

Foreword

This volume completes the trilogy I planned many years ago, as a basis for the study and practice of astrology.

In *The Astrologer's Astronomical Handbook* the raw materials, the tools and equipment, and the astronomical framework upon which is based the whole structure of astrological interpretation, are explained in detail. In *How to Read the Ephemeris* the student is helped to clearly understand that essential reference book, the *ephemeris*, without which no astrological chart could be erected.

The object of this third title in the trilogy is to enable the student to become quickly proficient at the calculation and erection of the natal chart. Because the entire book has been devoted to these calculations each necessary step in the construction of the natal chart has been carefully explained with examples. In the many years I have tutored students from more than ninety different countries I have become aware of the most common errors the beginner-student tends to make, and these have each been clearly pointed out.

This is the first astrological textbook devoted entirely to natal chart calculations which includes *exercises at the end of most chapters, whereby the student can test his understanding of what he has read in a particular chapter.* One hundred and twenty-two exercises can be worked on, and the correct answers are given at the back of the book—as good as having a tutor at one's elbow to correct test papers!

Practically all the calculations have been made with reference to pages reproduced from *Raphael's 1966 Ephemeris*, which is now based on *Ephemeris Time* and not *Greenwich Mean Time*. However, to avoid possible confusion, all times and calculations referred to in the *ephemeris*, throughout this book, are assumed to be Greenwich Mean Time. At the present time the difference between E.T. and G.M.T. is a mere 35 seconds.

Grateful acknowledgement is made to Margaret Hone, D.F.Astrol.S., for the DIRECT METHOD of natal chart calculation, first presented in her *The Modern Textbook of Astrology*, and which has been employed in this present volume.

The pages from *Raphael's 1966 Ephemeris* are strictly copyright and reproduced with the permission of the publishers, W. Foulsham & Co. Ltd. On no account must these pages be reproduced without prior consent of the publishers.

The Six Stages in Compiling
a Natal Chart

1. Converting *birth-time* into the corresponding *Greenwich Mean Time* (Chapter 3).

2. Finding the *local sidereal time at birth.*

   Step 1—Sidereal Time at noon G.M.T. (Chapter 4)
   Step 2—Interval between noon and birth (Chapter 5)
   Step 3—Acceleration on interval (Chapter 6)
   Step 4—Longitude equivalent in time (Chapter 7)
   Step 5—Additional adjustments for local sidereal time
          at birth *for Southern Hemisphere latitudes
          only* (Chapter 20)

3. Determining the *Ascendant, Midheaven, and house cusps* (Chapters 9–11).

4. Calculating the *planets' positions.*
   Step 1—Celestial longitude (Chapter 13)
   Step 2—Declination (Chapter 15)

5. Calculating and tabulating *planetary aspects.*
   Step 1—Inter-planetary aspects (in longitude)
          (Chapter 16)
   Step 2—Aspects to the angles (Chapter 16)
   Step 3—Inter-planetary aspects (in declination)
          (Chapter 16)

6. Classification of Chart Factors (Chapter 17).

Example Chart: The Basic Formula and Workings

Name:	Peter
Birth-date:	7th May 1966
Birthplace:	Oxford, England
Latitude:	51° 45′ N.
Longitude:	1° 15′ W.

Stage 1: TIME CONVERSION

		H.	M.	S.	
Birth-time as given	=	8	52	00	p.m.
Zone Standard (E −, W +)	=	0	00	00	
Summer (or Double) Time (−)	=	1	00	00	
G.M.T.	=	7	52	00	p.m.

G.M.T. date = 7th May 1966

Stage 2: FINDING LOCAL SIDEREAL TIME AT BIRTH

		H.	M.	S.
Sidereal time noon G.M.T.	=	2	59	31
Interval *TO/FROM noon $\left.\begin{array}{l}\text{*a.m. −}\\ \text{p.m. +}\end{array}\right\}$	=	7	52	00
Result =		10	51	31
Acceleration on interval $\left.\begin{array}{l}\text{*a.m. −}\\ \text{p.m. +}\end{array}\right\}$	=		1	18
Sidereal time at Greenwich at birth	=	10	52	49
Longitude equivalent in time $\left.\begin{array}{l}\text{*E +}\\ \text{W −}\end{array}\right\}$	=		5	00
Local sidereal time at birth	=	10	47	49

* Delete whichever is not required.

1 *What is a Natal Chart?*

Natal chart is the name given by astrologers to the plotted positions of the Sun, Moon, and planets as they are at a specified *moment in time*, relative to a specified *location* on Earth.

The old-fashioned term for an astrological chart, that has for many years been discarded by the trained astrological-consultant, was *horoscope*, derived from *hora* (an hour) and *scope* (to view).

The name *natal* chart strictly speaking refers to the chart for a human birth, but it can also apply to the chart calculated for a moment when *any thing begins.*

The astrologer needs to know the *time* factor and the *place* (space factor) of an event's occurrence to enable him to calculate a chart of the corresponding planetary pattern from a geocentric viewpoint. The necessary astronomical data are given in an *ephemeris* for any particular year. The *geocentric framework* for locating the positions of the planets relative to the Earth is fully illustrated and explained in *The Astrologer's Astronomical Handbook*.

The Symbolism of the Natal Chart

In Fig. 1 we see three different sized circles forming what appears to be a wheel, complete with twelve equally-spaced spokes. This is the basic framework of the natal chart.

The innermost and smallest circle symbolizes the *Earth* as the focal or central point of reference. As the chart is calculated for a specified *place* on the Earth's surface, that place must have a *horizon*. This horizon we know as the *visible* horizon. For calculation purposes this actual horizon is not used, but a great circle, the plane of which passes through the centre of the Earth and is parallel to the visible horizon is used. This is called the *true* horizon and it is a vital feature of the natal chart as shown in Fig. 1.

For convenience for measuring distant celestial bodies that are positioned *outside* the sphere of the Earth, the

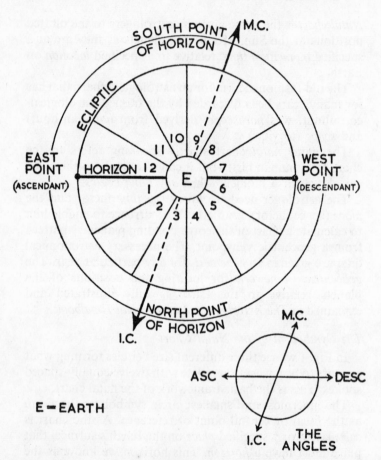

Fig. 1. The natal chart symbolizes the birth locality's relationship to the ecliptic.

plane of the true horizon is extended to infinity. This can be seen in Fig. 1 because the second largest circle symbolizes the *ecliptic*, and the horizon extends to this circle.

The ecliptic is the apparent path of the Sun around the Earth, and also the circle close to which lie the orbits of the planets. The *signs of the zodiac* (not to be confused with constellations bearing the same names) are twelve equal areas of the ecliptic. If you look at Fig. 7 you will see that the symbols for the twelve signs are always placed *outside* this circle that symbolizes the ecliptic, and the planets are entered *inside* the circle.

The ecliptic intersects the celestial horizon (which is the name for the true horizon extended to infinity) at the horizon's *east* point, the Ascendant of the chart, where the Sun, Moon and planets rise; and at the horizon's *west* point, the Descendant of the chart, where the Sun, Moon and planets set. The *south* point of the horizon is at the top of the chart, so called because if we stand facing south the Sun could be seen to rise at the east point of the horizon on our left, and eventually set in the west on our right. The *north* point of the horizon is therefore at the foot of the chart.

The third and largest circle shown in Fig. 1 does not symbolize anything but is merely the outer rim of the chart.

The lines in Fig. 1 that appear to be twelve equally-spaced "spokes" are what are known as the *cusps* of the twelve *houses* of the chart. The houses are fully explained in Chapter 11, and the reason for their numbering being in an anticlockwise direction. The *Midheaven* (M.C.) is where the ecliptic intersects the meridian circle of birth-place, and although it is in the "midheaven", where the Sun would be at its highest overhead, it will rarely be found to be plotted exactly on the 10th house cusp which is in line with the south point of the horizon, but will appear either to the left or the right of the 10th cusp. In Fig. 1 the M.C. is shown in the 9th house. The M.C. is also known as the *upper meridian*, and its opposite point in the chart is the *lower meridian* (I.C.).

When the positions of the Sun and planets have been calculated a useful check on the correctness of the calculated Ascendant is to find where the Sun will appear in the chart. Fig. 2 illustrates that if birth is around *sunrise* the

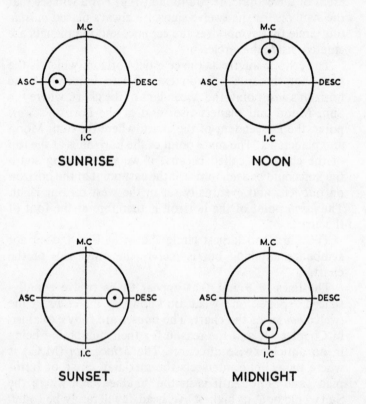

Fig. 2. Approximate positions of Sun in chart when birth occurs near sunrise, noon, sunset or midnight.

Sun should be near the Ascendant; if birth is around *noon* the Sun should be near the M.C.; if birth is around *sunset* the Sun should be near the Descendant; and if birth is around *midnight* the Sun should be near the I.C. If it is not, as the case may be—the student will have to recalculate the Ascendant!

2 *The Tools and Equipment*

When an astrologer sits at his desk to calculate a natal chart he will first have made sure that he has at his elbow his "tools and equipment" for doing the job properly:

(*a*) The birth-data, carefully checked.

(*b*) Chart-form.

(*c*) *Ephemeris* for year of birth.

(*d*) *Pluto Ephemeris* (if birth prior to 1934).

(*e*) *Tables of Houses.*

(*f*) Gazetteer.

(*g*) Lists or books giving Zone and Standard Times and Daylight Saving Times (Summer Times).

(*h*) Acceleration Table.

(*i*) Conversion of Arc to Time (tables).

(*j*) Ruler; compasses (type with a pencil in one end) or dividers; and, of course, scribbling pad and pen— preferably two ball-pens, one red, one blue or black.

The Birth-Data

The birth-data required are the *date*, the *time*, and the *place* of birth. This data should be carefully checked to ascertain that they are as accurate as can be known. Perhaps hours of calculation and interpretation could be wasted if the birth-data as given are later found to be inaccurate. If someone gives you their own data they may be pretty certain to be correct, yet if this is given in writing the wise astrologer still obtains confirmation of its correctness. It is all too easy to carelessly write figures incorrectly.

Misunderstandings can frequently occur regarding birth *time*. If this is merely stated as, say, "9.30", make sure that this is either *a.m.* or *p.m.* If the time is given as "17.30 hours" it will probably be correct to take it as meaning "5.30 p.m." This will apply to any time given as 13.00 hours or more. But do be extremely careful when the time is given as "12.30 a.m." or "12.30 p.m." This data *must* be confirmed. Does the writer mean 30 minutes after *midnight* when he writes "12.30 a.m.", or 30 minutes after *noon*?

12.30 a.m. = 30 minutes after *midnight*, beginning of day.
12.30 p.m. = 30 minutes after *noon*.

But don't just assume that the other person meant this too. I would advise students to get into the habit of writing these "12 o'clock times" as follows:

12.30 a.m. is written as 0.30 a.m.
12.30 p.m. is written as 0.30 p.m.

Particularly for students living in the United Kingdom another possible pitfall is when, for example, the birth *date* is received from an American source as *6.10.1932.* It would be quite understandable if the student set up the chart for *6th October 1932.* Yet how wrong he could be! With our American friends it is apparently the practice to write the *month* first and the date in that month second. Thus, *6.10.1932* would mean *10th June 1932.*

The *kind of time* must be clearly stated. It may be *local* time, *Zone* or *Standard* Time, *Daylight Saving* or *Summer* Time, or *Greenwich Mean* Time.

How many persons know their *exact* time of birth? Very few. It is advisable in most cases to request the probable *margin of error.* For instance, rather than be told birth was "about 5 p.m.", it would be better if one were told that birth was "about 5 p.m. with an error of 10 minutes either way". If necessary the chart can then be rectified to the possible time of birth by applying one of the various methods of rectification given in textbooks.

When the time of birth is *unknown,* and only the date of

birth can be used, a *flat* chart or *sunrise* chart may be set up (see Appendix V). Or, by obtaining a photograph of the person, and dates of important events in their life (deaths of close relatives, births of children, important changes and moves of residence, accidents, marriage, love affairs, etc.), and types of illness they may be prone to, the experienced astrologer can find clues as to the most likely signs on the Ascendant and M.C. as well as the degrees, from which he can find the speculative time of birth. Such a chart, however, *can only be speculative* and this must be clearly stated.

Chart-form

As a start the student can quite easily make his own chart-form, by drawing the circles and house cusps as shown in Fig. 1. But it is better and more efficient especially for making a collection of charts for filing if the properly printed forms are used—and, for filing purposes, always the same type of form. Recommended forms are detailed in Appendix III.

The Ephemeris

An *ephemeris* is a booklet, usually published annually, containing the ephemeral or momentary positions of the Sun, Moon, and planets. These are mostly calculated for noon Greenwich Mean Time, for Greenwich in England, for each day of a given year. The student will be learning how to use this data for births occurring anywhere on Earth and not just at Greenwich. Throughout this present book the pages of *Raphael's 1966 Ephemeris* will be referred to, and these annual ephemerides are recommended for all work.

Pluto Ephemeris

The positions of the planet Pluto are not given in *Raphael's Ephemerides* prior to 1934, as Pluto was not discovered until 1930. Therefore a separate ephemeris for Pluto for those earlier years is a necessity. See Appendix III.

Tables of Houses

As its name implies, this is a booklet containing tables connected with the *houses* of the birth-chart. These, and their use, are explained in Chapter 9. It is from these tables that the important Ascendant and M.C. can be found for a chart.

Gazetteer

The astrologer must know the terrestrial latitude and longitude for the birthplace of the individual whose chart he is to calculate. To assess these co-ordinates from an atlas is not the most reliable procedure if accuracy is desired. Not all atlases include a gazetteer section, where the correct co-ordinates for principal cities are listed.

Zone and Standard Time; Summer Time

The different categories of time in which the birth-moment may be given are:

1. Greenwich Mean Time.
2. Zone or Standard Time.
3. Local Mean Time.
4. Daylight Saving Time, or Summer Time.
5. Double Summer Time.

The first step in calculating a natal chart is to convert the given time of birth into Greenwich Mean Time (G.M.T.). If birth-time is given in G.M.T. no conversion is necessary. The reason why this conversion must be made is because most ephemerides are based on G.M.T. What the astrologer needs to know is the *exact variation of the given time from G.M.T.* so that the correct conversion into the corresponding G.M.T. can be made.

Space does not permit an adequate explanation of all the

world time variations and it will be necessary for the student to obtain books dealing with these. See Appendix III. In this present volume you will be shown examples of time-conversion.

Daylight Saving or *Summer* Time has been used by most principal countries for many years. Usually one hour is *added* to the normal time system employed during the summer months, though in some cases this has been added permanently. *Double Summer Time* (adding two hours to G.M.T.) was also used for periods during the war years in the United Kingdom. Unfortunately it is difficult to obtain a complete and accurate listing of *all* time variations that have been used throughout the world, and the student needs to be most careful to obtain as far as he can assess the correct time variation from G.M.T. operative at a given birth-moment.

Acceleration Table

A stage in the calculation of the local sidereal time at birth is called *acceleration on the interval* (Chapter 6). These tables are given for quick reference in Appendix I.

Conversion of Arc to Time

Another stage in the calculation of local sidereal time at birth is the conversion of degrees and minutes of *terrestrial longitude* into longitude equivalent in *time*. This is fully explained in Chapter 7, and tables for quick and accurate conversion are given in Appendix II.

Writing Tools and Material

Apart from the obvious pen and scribbling pad for notes and calculations, a ruler and compasses or dividers are needed for those who use the Equal House System. These will be for entering the "aspect-lines" (see Chapter 16). Aspect-lines are entered in two colours, so a blue or black and a red pen should be part of the equipment.

3 *Preparing the Birth-Data*

If you turn to Fig. 7 (p. 90) you will see the completed chart for a child we will call "Peter". This is going to be the main example chart we will dissect and learn how to calculate and construct as shown in the illustration.

As was noted in Chapter 1, the circular design of the birth-chart resembles a wheel, complete with spokes and hub. This is why we often speak of the *rim* of the chart, meaning the outer circle. Inside the outer circle or rim of the chart depicted in Fig. 7 are drawn the symbols of the twelve zodiacal signs. Inside the next, and smaller, circle you will see the symbols for the Sun, Moon, the eight planets, and the North and South Nodes of the Moon.

Written neatly against the planets' symbols (remember that the Sun and Moon *for convenience only* are usually called *planets* too) are their positions in terms of celestial longitude. These positions are measurement in degrees and minutes of longitude which tell us exactly where each planet was in the ecliptic at the moment when Peter was born. In the following chapters you will learn just how these figures for Peter's chart were arrived at.

So get your pen or pencil ready, because we are going to apply the first step in calculating Peter's chart, and *every calculation that we will do together in this book I want you to write down on your own notepaper, even though you may seem to be merely copying the figures that are printed. In this way you will be participating in every calculation, and not just reading about these.*

Peter's birth-data are given as:

> Date: 7th May 1966
> Time: 8.52 p.m. B.S.T.
> Place: Oxford, England

It doesn't look very much, does it?—when we consider that here is the KEY to understanding a great deal about the inner drives, temperament, and potential abilities of someone we have never met (assuming that our fictitious Peter were an actual person, and who would be yet, as I write this, just a squalling, suckling babe-in-arms!).

This data of *date*, *time*, and *place* of birth would correctly be entered on to the appropriate chart-form, and if you refer to Appendix III you will find information concerning printed forms that can be purchased from the publishers of this book. But if you have not yet bought any ready-to-use forms this does not matter for this present exercise. It is, however, best to stock a few dozen chart-forms and calculation-forms for your own practice and use. To always use the same type and size of chart-form is better for filing purposes. The recommended forms remind the student of the sequence of steps in calculation, because they are designed as a guide to correct calculation, and the completed chart should be a neat, easy-to-read, and businesslike presentation—giving the impression of an efficient astrologer. Besides, it can be messy, confusing, and inefficient to have numerous scraps of paper scribbled upon which represent the calculations and chart for each person whose data you work on.

Peter was born on the 7th May 1966, at Oxford in England. So at the top of our sheet of plain, or preferably lined, paper we write:

> Name: Peter
> Birth-date: 7th May 1966
> Birthplace: Oxford, England

Latitude and Longitude of Birthplace

We turn now to our *gazetteer*, to find what are the *latitude* and *longitude* of Oxford. Remember that this latitude and longitude are the co-ordinates for measuring the position on the Earth's surface of a given place, and are not to be confused with the co-ordinates of latitude and longitude we employ for locating a planet's position in the heavens for a given moment. Strictly speaking, the co-ordinates for measuring a given point or place on the Earth's surface should be called *terrestrial* latitude and *terrestrial* longitude; whilst the similar named co-ordinates that tell us the position of a planet with reference to the ecliptic are known as *celestial* latitude and *celestial* longitude.

All fair-sized gazetteers should list *Oxford*. In my gazetteer I find that Oxford is located at *51° 45' north*, and *1° 15' west*. Don't worry if these figures differ from those given in your gazetteer. The difference will only be very slight.

Not all gazetteers state which of the co-ordinates refer to latitude and which refer to longitude. This does not matter, since you will quickly learn (and probably know already) that the two cardinal points (of the compass) we call *north* and *south* refer to *terrestrial latitude*, whilst *east* and *west* refer to *terrestrial longitude*. Latitude is angular distance or measurement of a given place north or south of the *equator*. Oxford in England is, therefore, situated 51° 45' (51 degrees, 45 minutes) *north* of the Earth's equator. The second co-ordinate, which determines *where* along the parallel of latitude 51° 45' (which, of course, is visualized as encircling the Earth at that equal distance north of the equator) we will find Oxford situated, is longitude 1° 15' (1 degree, 15 minutes) *west*. The longitude of any given place is west or east (as the case may be) of the meridian of Greenwich.

We have found the co-ordinates we must use in the natal chart calculations for the birthplace of our example case,

Peter. So we enter these co-ordinates on our notepaper. The data we have so far written will look like this:

> Name: Peter
> Birth-date: 7th May 1966
> Birthplace: Oxford, England
> Latitude: 51° 45′ N.
> Longitude: 1° 15′ W.

Converting Birth-time to G.M.T.

The next calculation step concerns young Peter's *time* of birth. This is given as 8.52 p.m. B.S.T. We are now at a stage in our calculations when it is so easy to make a mistake that could cause all the calculations that follow, and are based on this important time factor, to be wrong. We must be absolutely sure of what we are doing.

In Peter's case we are dealing with a birth in England, or, more broadly speaking, in the United Kingdom of Great Britain. This fact simplifies our task and lessens the risk of error in time calculation. This is because since 1916 a birth occurring in the United Kingdom would be given correctly in one of three time categories:

1. *G.M.T.* or Greenwich Mean Time.
2. *B.S.T.* or British Summer Time (1 hour in advance of G.M.T.).
3. *D.B.S.T.* or Double British Summer Time (2 hours in advance of G.M.T.).

What we have to do is convert the time of birth, if necessary, into *Greenwich Mean Time* (G.M.T.). If the time is given to us in terms of G.M.T. then we have no conversion to do. In Peter's case we read that birth was 8.52 p.m. B.S.T. In other words, at his birth in May 1966 British Summer Time was operative. B.S.T. is *one hour in advance* of G.M.T., or put another way, it is G.M.T. plus one hour. All we have to do to obtain Peter's birth-time in G.M.T. is *subtract* one hour from 8.52 p.m., which gives us 7.52 p.m. G.M.T.

We must write down this simple calculation correctly, so that this step is perfectly clear. We write this directly beneath the data we have already listed on our notepaper (*H.M.S.* standing for *hours, minutes, seconds* in time):

TIME CONVERSION		H.	M.	S.	
Birth-time as given	=	8	52	00	p.m.
Zone Standard (E –, W +)	=	0	00	00	
Summer (or Double) Time (–)	=	1	00	00	
G.M.T.	=	7	52	00	p.m.

G.M.T. date = 7th May 1966

When you buy the blank chart-forms (nos. 1 and 2) recommended in Appendix III you will see that "Zone Standard" is necessarily included at this stage in the calculations dealing with time conversion. The term *Zone Standard* as given here means "Zone Standard Time difference from G.M.T." This factor is ignored for births other than those occurring in countries where Zone Standard Time is employed. Whilst you are not using the printed chart-forms it is as well to always include Zone Standard as given above, even if, as in Peter's case (because born in the U.K.), it can be ignored. Getting into this habit ensures that when you *do* need to apply this conversion of Zone Standard Time difference from G.M.T. you do not forget to do so, because it will be a part of your thinking to always note whether it is to be ignored or not.

The initial stage in calculating Peter's birth-chart is now completed: the *preparation of the birth-data*:

Name:	Peter
Birth-date:	7th May 1966
Birthplace:	Oxford, England
Latitude:	51° 45′ N.
Longitude:	1° 15′ W.

TIME CONVERSION		*H.*	*M.*	*S.*	
Birth-time as given	=	8	52	00	p.m.
Zone Standard (E −, W +)	=	0	00	00	
Summer (or Double) Time (−)	=	1	00	00	
G.M.T.	=	7	52	00	p.m.

G.M.T. date = 7th May 1966

We have prepared the data for Peter's birth, in terms of exact co-ordinates for the birth *place*, and in terms of *Greenwich Mean Time*. We are ready to learn about the next step, the *calculation of local sidereal time at birth*. This is fully explained in Chapters 4–7.

When G.M.T. Changes Birth-date

It sometimes happens that in converting the given birth-time into G.M.T. the actual *date* of birth is changed. Mostly this will be found to happen with births outside the United Kingdom, where the Zone Standard Time employed in a country, or in a section of a large country, differs by several hours from G.M.T.

For example, a birth occurs at 9.0 p.m. E.S.T. (Eastern Standard Time) in New York (Long. 74° *west* of Greenwich), on the 10th January 1966. Daylight Saving Time is not in operation. E.S.T. varies from G.M.T. by 5 hours. But are these 5 hours in *advance* of or *behind* G.M.T.? Referring to what we have written above, when listing Peter's completed data, regarding "Zone Standard Time difference from G.M.T." we note that in brackets it is stated (E −, W +). This tells us that when the place of birth (using Zone Standard Time) is *east* of the Greenwich meridian, we *subtract* the Zone Standard Time difference from G.M.T. from the birth-time to obtain the corresponding G.M.T. But when the birthplace is *west* of Greenwich we must *add* the Zone Standard Time difference from G.M.T. to the birth-time to convert it to G.M.T.

In our present example, the birthplace is New York, and if you have the necessary Standard Time tables by you (such as those given in my *Teach Yourself Astrology*) you will note that Eastern Standard Time used in New York is *5 hours slow on G.M.T.* Thus, as the longitude for New York is *west* of Greenwich we must *add* 5 hours to the birth-time to convert it to G.M.T. As follows:

> Birth-time = 9.00 p.m. E.S.T. (10th January)
> (add) + 5.00
> ————
> G.M.T. = 2.00 a.m.   (11th January)

In adding 5 hours to 9.00 p.m. we find that 9.00 + 3 hours brings the time to midnight on the 10th January, and adding the further 2 hours (3 + 2 = 5) makes the time 2 a.m. on the 11th January. Yes, you can see what has happened—whereas the time of birth in terms of Eastern Standard Time fell on the 10th January in New York, the corresponding Greenwich Mean Time would occur on the 11th January!

This is why the student must always enter the *G.M.T. date* beneath the G.M.T. for birth, as has been done in Peter's case. Making a habit of this will lessen the risk of using the local or Standard Time date by mistake, when it differs from the G.M.T. date, in the calculation of local sidereal time at birth and for the planetary positions.

Similarly, the date may change at the beginning of the day when converting birth-time into G.M.T. This can sometimes happen when:

(*a*) Daylight Saving Time or Summer Time is *subtracted*.
(*b*) Birthplace is *east* of Greenwich, therefore Zone Standard Time difference from G.M.T. is *subtracted* from birth-time.

Here is an example for (*a*): Birth occurs at 0.30 a.m. B.S.T. on the 6th May 1960, in London. B.S.T. tells us that Summer Time is operating. So we need to *subtract one hour* from the given birth-time to convert to G.M.T. By so doing we find that in terms of G.M.T. birth actually occurs at 11.30 p.m. on the *previous* day, 5th May.

And now for an example for (*b*). Birth occurs at 5.0 a.m. on the 5th March 1966, at Sydney (Long. 151° 10′ *east* of Greenwich) in Australia. The Zone Standard Time difference from G.M.T. is 10 hours. As Sydney is *east* of Greenwich in terms of terrestrial longitude the difference of 10 hours must be *subtracted* from the birth-time to convert this into G.M.T. As follows:

Birth-time   =   5.00 a.m. Standard Time (5th March)
 (minus) –   =   10.00
                        ───────
G.M.T.   =   7.00 p.m.   (4th March)

For those readers who may have some difficulty in understanding how *10* hours can be subtracted from a lesser number (*5* hours a.m.) to arrive at 7.0 p.m., a little explanation may help. As *10* cannot be directly subtracted from *5*, we add one whole day of *24* hours to *5*. In effect this is like calling the previous day "24.00 hours", and then adding to it 5 hours (the interval from midnight to 5.0 a.m.). Thus, 24 hours + 5 hours = 29 hours. Subtracting 10 hours from 29 hours = 19 hours. If 12.00 hours = noon; 13.00 hours (12 + 1) = 1.0 p.m.; then it follows that 19.00 hours (12 + 7) = 7.0 p.m.

Why Convert Birth-time to G.M.T.?

Before we venture into the next chapter, let us make fully sure that we have understood the procedure detailed in this present chapter.

The only reason why we need to convert local time or Standard Time or Daylight Saving Time (Summer Time) into G.M.T. is because practically all the ephemerides used by astrologers today are based on G.M.T. In this book we are referring only to data given in *Raphael's 1966 Ephemeris*, unless otherwise stated. Once we know what a given time of birth *corresponds to in G.M.T.* we can go ahead and apply this G.M.T. for birth to the measurements in sidereal time and planetary co-ordinates as listed *for noon G.M.T.* on the desired day or days in *Raphael's Ephemeris*.

You can now test yourself to find whether you have understood what you have read in this chapter. The answers to these exercises can be found in Appendix VII.

What is the Greenwich Mean Time, and the Greenwich Mean Time *date*, corresponding to the following birth-times?

1. 4.23 p.m. B.S.T., 11th July 1938, London, England.
2. 1.14 p.m. D.B.S.T., 28th April 1945, Exeter, England.
3. 0.37 a.m. B.S.T., 1st June 1957, Hitchin, England.
4. 0.00 p.m. (noon) E.S.T., 22nd March 1965, New York, U.S.A. (Long. 74° W.). Zone Standard Time 5 hours slow on G.M.T.
5. 10.35 p.m. E.S.T., 22nd March 1965, New York, U.S.A. (Long. 74° W.). Zone Standard Time 5 hours slow on G.M.T.
6. 5.22 p.m., 10th June 1966, Sydney, Australia (151° 10′ E.). Zone Standard Time 10 hours fast on G.M.T.
7. 3.40 a.m., 20th May 1960, Sydney, Australia (151° 10′ E.). Zone Standard Time 10 hours fast on G.M.T.

4 *Finding Local Sidereal Time (1)*

Step 1—Sidereal Time at Noon G.M.T.

We will begin this chapter by again turning to Fig. 7 (p. 90), that shows the completed chart for our example case, Peter.

On the left-hand side of Peter's chart you will read the capital letters *ASC*. These are the astrologer's usual abbreviation for *Ascendant*. In normal practice the astrologer does not bother to enter *ASC* in this way, because he already knows where the Ascendant is in the chart. Near the top of the chart are the capital letters *MC*. This is the abbreviation for *Midheaven* (or *Medium Coeli*), and astrologers using the Equal House System always enter *M.C.* with an arrow against the degree of the ecliptic that is "culminating at the Midheaven" at the time on which the chart is based.

The degrees of the ecliptic that are found by calculation to occupy the Ascendant and Midheaven respectively at a given moment, determine the vital *angles* of the chart (see Fig. 1).

Local Sidereal Time: the Key to Ascendant and Midheaven

The *sidereal day* is the exact period of rotation of the Earth on its axis, measured in terms of sidereal time between two successive transits of the First Point of Aries over the observer's upper meridian. *Sidereal time* is then exactly OH.OOM.OOS. for that meridian. This OH.OOM. OOS. reading is purely in terms of sidereal time reckoning, and it may correspond to any hour of the day or night as reckoned by clock time.

The beginner-student will not be expected to fully grasp

what has just been said concerning sidereal time, but he will be a better and wiser astrologer who has even an elementary understanding of the derivation of the figures he employs in the calculation of a natal chart.[1]

When we speak of *local* sidereal time we are referring to sidereal time as it is measured for a *particular meridian*.

The *second stage* in the calculation of a natal chart (see p. 9) is to *find the local sidereal time at birth*. In the case of our example birth-data, when the local sidereal time corresponding to the moment and the place of birth is known, we will be able to find the Ascendant and Mid-heaven for Peter's natal chart. We will be able to insert the sign and the degree and minute relative to each of the 12 house cusps. The basic framework of the natal chart will then have been ascertained, preliminary to entering the planets when their respective positions in the ecliptic have been calculated.

Sidereal Time Found in the Ephemeris

The local sidereal time *for all places on the Greenwich meridian* (Longitude 0° 00′) are shown for noon G.M.T. each day in *Raphael's Ephemeris* for any given year. This means that if we want to know the local sidereal time at *noon* G.M.T. for Greenwich in England on the 7th May 1966 (Peter's birthday) we must obtain *Raphael's 1966 Ephemeris*.

Figures 3 and 4 are reproductions of the two pages from *Raphael's 1966 Ephemeris* covering the thirty-one days of May. We are at this moment particularly interested in the lower section of Fig. 3.

What was the sidereal time at Greenwich corresponding to noon G.M.T. on the day of Peter's birth, 7th May 1966?

We have to find the 7th May. So we refer to Fig. 3, because here we have the left-hand page for May, containing the sidereal time readings for each day of that

---

[1] See *The Astrologer's Astronomical Handbook*, Chapters 7 and 8.

10						MAY, 1966						[*RAPHAEL'S*

D M	Neptune Lat.	Dec.	Herschel Lat.	Dec.	Saturn Lat.	Dec.	Jupiter Lat.	Dec.	Mars Lat.	Dec.	
1	1 N49	16 S 17	0 N48	6 N22	1 S 58	3 S 28	0 S 3	23 N24	0 S 11	14 N41	14 N56
3	1 49	16 17	0 48	6 23	1 59	3 24	0 3	23 24	0 10	15 10	15 24
5	1 49	16 16	0 48	6 24	1 59	3 20	0 3	23 24	0 8	15 38	15 52
7	1 49	16 15	0 48	6 25	1 59	3 16	0 2	23 24	0 7	16 5	16 19
9	1 49	16 14	0 47	6 25	2 0	3 12	0 2	23 24	0 6	16 32	16 45
11	1 49	16 13	0 47	6 26	2 0	3 8	0 2	23 24	0 4	16 58	17 11
13	1 49	16 12	0 47	6 26	2 1	3 4	0 2	23 24	0 3	17 24	17 36
15	1 49	16 12	0 47	6 26	2 1	3 0	0 2	23 24	0 2	17 49	18 1
17	1 49	16 11	0 47	6 26	2 1	2 56	0 1	23 24	0 1	18 13	18 24
19	1 49	16 10	0 47	6 27	2 2	2 53	0 1	23 24	0 N 1	18 36	18 47
21	1 49	16 9	0 47	6 27	2 2	2 50	0 1	23 23	0 2	18 59	19 10
23	1 49	16 8	0 47	6 27	2 3	2 46	0 1	23 23	0 3	19 21	19 31
25	1 48	16 7	0 47	6 27	2 3	2 43	0 0	23 23	0 5	19 42	19 52
27	1 48	16 7	0 47	6 26	2 4	2 40	0 0	23 22	0 6	20 2	20 12
29	1 48	16 6	0 47	6 26	2 4	2 37	0 0	23 21	0 7	20 22	20 31
31	1 48	16 5	0 47	6 26	2 5	2 35	0 0	23 20	0 8	20 40	

D M	D W	Sidereal Time H. M. S.	☉ Long.	☉ Dec.	☽ Long.	☽ Lat.	☽ Dec.	MIDNIGHT ☽ Long.	☽ Dec.
1	☉	2 35 52	10 ♉ 39 31	15 N 1	25 ♍ 26 38	4 N33	5 N59	2 ♎ 42 31	2 N46
2	M	2 39 48	11 37 43	15 20	9 ♎ 57 48	3 45	0 S 30	17 11 45	3 S 45
3	Tu	2 43 45	12 35 53	15 37	24 23 38	2 43	6 56	1 ♏ 32 46	10 1
4	W	2 47 41	13 34 1	15 55	8 ♏ 38 30	1 31	12 57	15 40 16	15 41
5	Th	2 51 38	14 32 8	16 12	22 37 34	0 15	18 12	29 30 1	20 26
6	F	2 55 34	15 30 13	16 29	6 ♐ 17 20	1 S 1	22 21	12 ♐ 59 20	23 57
7	S	2 59 31	16 28 16	16 46	19 35 57	2 11	25 12	26 7 14	26 6
8	☉	3 3 28	17 26 18	17 2	2 ♑ 33 20	3 12	26 37	8 ♑ 54 27	26 47
9	M	3 7 24	18 24 18	17 19	15 10 56	4 4	25 14	3 ♒ 36 29	24 7
10	Tu	3 11 21	19 22 17	17 35	27 31 29	4 40	25 14	3 ♒ 36 29	24 7
11	W	3 15 17	20 20 15	17 50	9 ♒ 38 40	5 5	22 44	15 38 33	21 7
12	Th	3 19 14	21 18 11	18 5	21 36 43	5 16	19 17	27 33 44	17 16
13	F	3 23 10	22 16 6	18 20	3 ♓ 30 12	5 14	15 5	9 ♓ 26 39	12 46
14	S	3 27 7	23 14 0	18 35	15 23 41	4 58	10 22	21 21 48	7 43
15	☉	3 31 3	24 11 53	18 50	27 21 33	4 29	5 10	3 ♈ 23 24	2 28
16	M	3 35 0	25 9 44	19 4	9 ♈ 27 47	3 48	0 N16	15 35 6	3 N 1
17	Tu	3 38 57	26 7 34	19 17	21 45 43	2 56	5 46	27 59 55	8 30
18	W	3 42 53	27 5 23	19 31	4 ♉ 17 57	1 54	11 10	10 ♉ 39 58	13 45
19	Th	3 46 50	28 3 10	19 44	17 6 7	0 46	16 13	23 36 26	18 31
20	F	3 50 46	29 0 57	19 57	0 ♊ 10 55	0 N27	20 38	6 ♊ 49 27	22 30
21	S	3 54 43	29 58 42	20 9	13 31 57	1 39	24 4	20 18 12	25 19
22	☉	3 58 39	0 ♊ 56 25	20 21	27 7 58	2 47	26 12	4 ♋ 0 59	26 41
23	M	4 2 36	1 54 7	20 33	10 ♋ 56 56	3 46	26 45	17 55 30	26 24
24	Tu	4 6 32	2 51 48	20 44	24 56 20	4 33	25 37	1 ♌ 59 5	24 26
25	W	4 10 29	3 49 27	20 55	9 ♌ 3 24	5 4	22 52	16 8 55	20 58
26	Th	4 14 26	4 47 5	21 6	23 15 18	5 16	18 44	0 ♍ 22 13	16 15
27	F	4 18 22	5 44 41	21 16	7 ♍ 29 21	5 9	13 32	14 36 22	10 39
28	S	4 22 19	6 42 16	21 26	21 42 58	4 43	7 37	28 48 50	4 30
29	☉	4 26 15	7 39 49	21 36	5 ♎ 53 40	4 0	1 20	12 ♎ 57 11	1 S 50
30	M	4 30 12	8 37 21	21 45	19 59 3	3 3	4 S 59	26 58 59	8 4
31	Tu	4 34 8	9 34 51	21 54	3 ♏ 56 41	1 55	11 1	10 ♏ 51 49	13 50

Fig. 3.

© W. Foulsham & Co. Ltd.

FULL MOON—May 4, 9*h*. 1*m*. *p.m.*

D M	Venus Lat. ° ′	Venus Declin. ° ′	Venus Declin. ° ′	Mercury Lat. ° ′	Mercury Declin. ° ′	Mercury Declin. ° ′	☽ Node ° ′
1	1 S 5	2 S 36	2 S 13	2 S 47	4 N 4	4 N 40	26 ♉ 16
3	1 12	1 50	1 27	2 42	5 17	5 55	26 10
5	1 19	1 4	0 41	2 35	6 34	7 14	26 3
7	1 25	0 17	0 N 7	2 26	7 55	8 36	25 57
9	1 31	0 N 31	0 54	2 14	9 18	10 0	25 51
11	1 36	1 18	1 43	2 1	10 44	11 28	25 44
13	1 41	2 7	2 31	1 46	12 12	12 56	25 38
15	1 46	2 55	3 20	1 29	13 40	14 24	25 32
17	1 50	3 44	4 9	1 11	15 9	15 53	25 25
19	1 53	4 33	4 58	0 51	16 37	17 20	25 19
21	1 57	5 22	5 47	0 31	18 2	18 44	25 13
23	1 59	6 11	6 36	0 10	19 24	20 3	25 6
25	2 2	7 0	7 24	0 N 11	20 41	21 17	25 0
27	2 4	7 48	8 13	0 32	21 50	22 22	24 54
29	2 5	8 37	9 1	0 52	22 52	23 19	24 47
31	2 6	9 24		1 10	23 44		24 41

Mutual Aspects

1. ☉∠♄. ☿Q♃. ♀☌♄.
2. ♂∠♄.
4. ☿±♅, ▽♆, ±♇.
5. ☉P♆. ☿P♅. ♀□♃.
6. ☉∠♃, △♅, △♇.
7. ☿⊻♄. 8. ♂△♅, P♆.
9. ☿⚼♅. ♂∠♃, △♇.
10. ☿✱♃. ⚼♇. ♀⚼♆.
11. ☉☍♆. ☿⊥♄.
15. ♀P♄. ♂☍♆.
16. ☉P♇. ☿⊻♀, ∠♄.
17. ☉⊥♃, ☿△♅.
18. ☉✱♄. ☿∠♃, P♆, △♇. [♀±♆.
19. ♀▽♅, ▽♇. 20. ☿☍♆.
22. ☿⊥♂, ☌♂. ♀⊥♂. ♂P♇. ♃Q♅. 23. ☿P♂, ⊥♃, ✱♄, P♇. ♀▽♆.
24. ♀Q♃, ±♅, P♅, ±♇.
25. ☉⊻♃. [♃Q♇. ♅Stat.
26. ☉P☿. ☿⊻♃. ♂⊥♃. ✱♄.
27. ☉☌☿. ♇Stat.
29. ☿Q♄ 30. ☿P♃. ♀⊻♄.
31. ☿∠♀, □♅, □♇. ♃⚼♆.

D M	♆ Long. ° ′	♅ Long. ° ′	♄ Long. ° ′	♃ Long. ° ′	♂ Long. ° ′	♀ Long. ° ′	☿ Long. ° ′
S	21 ♏ 6	15 ♍ 42	25 ♓ 49	29 ♊ 14	10 ♉ 8	25 ♓ 58	16 ♈ 52
2	21 ℞ 4	15 ℞ 41	25 55	29 25	10 52	27 3	18 23
3	21 2	15 40	26 1	29 36	11 37	28 9	19 55
4	21 1	15 39	26 7	29 48	12 21	29 15	21 29
5	20 59	15 38	26 13	29 59	13 5	0 ♈ 21	23 5
6	20 58	15 37	26 18	0 ♋ 10	13 49	1 27	24 43
7	20 56	15 36	26 24	0 22	14 33	2 34	26 23
S	20 54	15 35	26 30	0 34	15 16	3 40	28 5
9	20 53	15 34	26 35	0 45	16 0	4 47	29 48
10	20 51	15 34	26 41	0 57	16 44	5 54	1 ♉ 34
11	20 49	15 33	26 46	1 9	17 28	7 1	3 22
12	20 48	15 32	26 51	1 21	18 11	8 8	5 11
13	20 46	15 32	26 57	1 33	18 55	9 15	7 3
14	20 44	15 31	27 2	1 45	19 38	10 22	8 56
S	20 43	15 31	27 7	1 57	20 22	11 30	10 52
16	20 41	15 30	27 12	2 9	21 5	12 37	12 49
17	20 40	15 30	27 17	2 21	21 49	13 45	14 48
18	20 38	15 30	27 22	2 33	22 32	14 53	16 49
19	20 36	15 30	27 27	2 46	23 15	16 1	18 52
20	20 35	15 29	27 32	2 58	23 58	17 9	20 56
21	20 33	15 29	27 36	3 10	24 42	18 17	23 2
S	20 32	15 29	27 41	3 23	25 25	19 25	25 10
23	20 30	15 29	27 46	3 36	26 8	20 34	27 19
24	20 28	15 D 29	27 50	3 48	26 51	21 42	29 28
25	20 27	15 29	27 54	4 1	27 34	22 50	1 ♊ 39
26	20 25	15 29	27 59	4 13	28 17	23 59	3 50
27	20 24	15 29	28 3	4 26	29 0	25 8	6 2
28	20 22	15 30	28 7	4 39	29 42	26 16	8 14
S	20 21	15 30	28 11	4 52	0 ♊ 25	27 25	10 26
30	20 19	15 30	28 15	5 4	1 8	28 34	12 37
31	20 18	15 31	28 19	5 17	1 51	29 43	14 48

Lunar Aspects

D M	☉	♇	♆	♅	♄	♃	♂	♀	☿
S	⚼		✱		☍	□	⚼	☍	
2		⊻	∠	⊻					
3		∠	⊻	∠		△			☍
4	☍			✱	⚼	⚼	☍	⚼	
5		✱	☌		△				
6								△	⚼
7		□	⊻	□					
S	⚼		∠		□	☍	⚼	□	△
9	△	△	✱	△			△		
10		⚼		⚼	✱				□
11					∠			✱	
12	□		□		⊻	⚼	□	∠	
13						△			✱
14		☍	△	☍			✱	⊻	
S	✱				☌	□			∠
16	∠		⚼				∠	☌	⊻
17	⊻				⊻		⊻		
18		⚼		⚼		✱			
19		△	☍	△	∠	∠		⊻	☌
20	☌				✱	⊻	☌	∠	
21		□		□				✱	
S	⊻				□	☌	⊻		⊻
23	∠	✱	⚼	✱			∠		∠
24		∠	△	∠	△		✱	□	✱
25	✱	⊻		⊻	⚼	⊻			
26			□			∠	□	△	
27	□					✱		⚼	□
28		☌	✱	☌	☍				
S	△		∠			□	△		△
30	⚼	⊻	⊻	⊻			⚼		
31		∠		∠		△		☍	⚼

LAST QUARTER—May 12, 11*h*. 19*m*. *a.m.*

Fig. 4.

month. Readers who have my *How to Read the Ephemeris* will already be conversant with the columns of data given on the two pages for each month.

In the lower portion of Fig. 3, the first column is headed D M, and the second column is headed D W. *D* stands for *day*, *M* stands for *month*. Thus, in the first column will be found the thirty-one *days of the month* of May 1966. The second column has little cause to be used. The *D* in this column stands for *day*, and the *W* stands for *week*: thus, the days of the week.

It is a simple matter to find "7" in the *first* column, indicating the 7th May.

I suggest that you make a *light* pencil stroke against this date, as a guide, also as a safeguard to ensure that you do not use the wrong date in error—this can easily be done—because you will be referring many times to the various columns of figures for the 7th May. This is a tip to remember each time you calculate a fresh birth-chart. If you make a *light* pencil mark this can be erased when you have completed the calculations.

We can now find *sidereal time*. At the top of the *third* column we clearly read *Sidereal Time*. This column contains three columns of figures. The first of these is headed by the capital letter *H*, meaning *hours*. The second column of figures is headed by a capital letter *M*, meaning *minutes*; and the third column of figures is directly under the capital *S*, meaning *seconds*. *H.M.S.* tells us, therefore, that sidereal time is expressed in *hours*, *minutes* and *seconds*.

We can now read the sidereal time measurement on Peter's birthday, 7th May 1966, *but for Greenwich, at noon G.M.T.*:

2.59.31

In other words, the sidereal time we are looking for is *2 hours 59 minutes 31 seconds*. As this is the reading for the Greenwich meridian at noon G.M.T. we could also correctly think of this as the *local* sidereal time *for Greenwich* at noon. Sidereal time reckoning for a given place begins (each day) the moment the First Point of Aries is on the upper meridian. Thus, it is *2 hours 59 minutes 31 seconds* in terms of sidereal time since the First Point of Aries "crossed" the upper meridian at Greenwich. Put in another way, measurement westwards along the arc of the equator in terms of sidereal time from the Greenwich upper meridian to the First Point of Aries is 2 hours 59 minutes 31 seconds.

In the next chapter we will learn how sidereal time at Greenwich for noon G.M.T. is entered into the calculations for Peter's natal chart.

Exercises

The answers to these exercises can be found in Appendix VII.

Referring to Fig. 3, what is sidereal time at noon G.M.T. corresponding to each of the following G.M.T. dates?

8. 1st May 1966.
9. 2nd May 1966.
10. 10th May 1966.
11. 22nd May 1966.

What is the *local* sidereal time for Greenwich at noon G.M.T. on the following dates?

12. 1st May 1966.
13. 8th May 1966.

How long is it, in terms of sidereal time, since the First Point of Aries was on the Greenwich upper meridian when it is noon G.M.T. on the following dates?

14. 1st May 1966.
15. 28th May 1966.

What is the sidereal time measurement westwards along

the arc of the equator *from* the Greenwich upper meridian *to* the First Point of Aries at noon G.M.T. on the following dates?

16. 1st May 1966.
17. 15th May 1966.

5 Finding Local Sidereal Time (2)

Step 2—Interval Between Noon and Birth

Before commencing the second step towards finding the local sidereal time at birth, it will be an apt moment to refresh our memory as to the *reason* for these calculations. *We want to know what are the Ascendant, the Midheaven, and the signs and degrees on each of the house cusps.* Until we know these factors we cannot enter the planets "in the chart". The *angles* of the chart (Asc.–Desc. axis, and the M.C.–I.C. axis) provide the basic orientation for the planetary patterns and zodiacal signs that make the chart a personal "blueprint" of potentialities for the individual concerned.

The Interval Value

We have shown in the previous chapter that the sidereal time given in the ephemeris for 7th May 1966 (2H.59M. 31S.) is for the Greenwich meridian as at noon G.M.T. We also remember that since this is for Greenwich we can also call this reading the *local* sidereal time *for Greenwich* at noon.

But as Peter, our example birth case, was not born at *noon* in terms of G.M.T., but at 7.52 p.m., the next step in our calculations is to find what is the *local sidereal time at Greenwich* at 7.52 p.m. G.M.T.

Note, however, that as yet we are not making any calculation for Peter having been born in *Oxford*. This will be done in Chapter 7. At this present step in our calculations it is necessary to compute the local sidereal time as though birth had been at 7.52 p.m. G.M.T. at *Greenwich*. The only reason for doing this is because to find the local sidereal time for Oxford we have first to work on the basic sidereal time reading given *for Greenwich* in the ephemeris.

Referring to this next step in the formula given on p. 10, we read the following:

H. M. S.

$$\text{Interval } *\text{TO/FROM noon} \quad \left. \begin{array}{l} *\text{a.m.} \ - \\ \text{p.m.} \ + \end{array} \right\}$$

The term *interval* refers to the interval of time between the birth moment and noon when birth occurs *before* noon; or the interval between noon and the birth moment when birth occurs *after* noon.

This is a relatively simple calculation and few beginner-students are likely to find this confusing to understand. But *do be careful*. Sometimes it is in doing the simplest calculations that the student makes a *careless* mistake. This particularly applies to the calculation of the interval when birth occurs in the morning, before noon.

Interval Value for Birth Before Noon

Let us assume that a birth occurs at 6.30 a.m. G.M.T. In the formula for Step 2 that we have just written down (and I hope that you *too* have written this down), we note that there is an *asterisk* placed against the word TO, and another asterisk against *a.m.* In the chart-forms recommended to students (Appendix III) there is a note entered at the foot of the form, to the effect that these two asterisks denote words that must be *deleted* if not required. If birth were *a.m.* we would delete (by putting a firm line through) the word FROM and the letters *p.m.* The formula for Step 2 would then read,

Interval TO *noon, a.m.* –

This would mean that birth occurring in the morning, the *interval in time* will be that from the birth moment *to* noon.

The minus sign (–) reminds us that when birth occurs in the *a.m.* the interval from birth-time *to* noon has to be *subtracted* from the sidereal time at Greenwich noon.

As an example of a birth occurring in the morning we have, a couple of paragraphs ago, assumed this to be 6.30 a.m. G.M.T. Noon corresponds to *12* hours. On a scrap of notepaper we write:

	H.	M.	
	12	00	(noon)
Subtract	6	30	(a.m.)
Answer =	5	30	(interval)

For those students who may be out of practice where even the simplest calculations are concerned we will work out the subtraction of 6 hours 30 minutes from 12 hours. We cannot subtract 30 minutes from 00 minutes, so we "borrow" *one whole hour* of 60 minutes. We are then able to subtract 30 minutes from these 60 borrowed minutes, which leaves 30 minutes "left over". We enter "30" under the *M.* (minutes) column. As we have "borrowed" one hour we have to make an adjustment to the noon (12 hours) time given. We have to "take away" this 1 hour that we borrowed. Thus: 12 hours minus 1 hour = 11 hours. We can now do the straightforward subtraction of 6 hours from 11 hours. The answer, of course, is 5 hours. The "5" is entered under the *H.* (hours) column as shown above.

Therefore when birth is 6.30 a.m., the *interval value* required is 5 hours 30 minutes. Again for those students who are not at all confident of even the simplest arithmetic they do, I would suggest as a further check that they *add* the interval value arrived at and the time of birth. The answer, if correct, should be equal to 12 hours noontime. As follows:

$$
\begin{array}{lll}
 & & H. \ M. \\
\text{Birth-time} & = & 6 \quad 30 \text{ a.m.} \\
\text{Interval value} & = & 5 \quad 30 \\
\hline
\text{Sum} & = & 12 \quad 00 \text{ noon}
\end{array}
$$

30 minutes plus 30 minutes = 60 minutes, or 1 hour. 5 hours plus 6 hours plus the 1 hour carried over from the minutes column = 12 hours.

A few paragraphs back I said that it is particularly easy for a beginner-student to make a *careless* error when calculating the interval between a *morning* birth-time and noon. On a number of occasions I have known beginners to write the interval as *6 hours 30 minutes* when birth is 6.30 a.m. This has not been due to not knowing that 6 hours 30 minutes have to be subtracted from 12 hours noon-time to find the correct interval value. The error has been quite simply a case of *carelessness*, when the student relaxes his concentration on what he should be doing.

We will quickly calculate another example of how to find the interval value for a morning birth. Let us assume that the birth-time is 1.47 a.m. G.M.T. See if you can get the same answer that I show here:

$$
\begin{array}{lll}
 & H. \ M. & \\
 & 12 \quad 00 & \text{(noon)} \\
\text{Subtract} & 1 \quad 47 & \text{(a.m.)} \\
\hline
 & 10 \quad 13 & \text{(interval)}
\end{array}
$$

Thus, when birth occurs at 1.47 a.m. G.M.T. the interval value, or the time-lapse from birth to noon, will be 10 hours 13 minutes.

Interval Value for Birth After Noon

We will now explain how to find the *interval value* for a birth occurring *after* noon (p.m.), and our example birth-time for Peter can be used.

Birth is given as 7.52 p.m. G.M.T.

As birth is *p.m.* we speak of the interval being *from* noon to the birth-time. This means that we subtract noon-time from the birth-time. But whereas noon was called 12.00 hours when we had to subtract a morning birth-time from noon-time, we now (for convenience) call noon 0.00 p.m.

		H.	*M.*
Peter's birth-time G.M.T.	=	7	52 p.m.
Noon G.M.T. (–)	=	0	00 p.m.
Interval value	=	7	52

P.M. Birth: Noon Sidereal Time plus Interval Value

We have found the interval value for Peter's birth to be 7 hours 52 minutes. Referring to the formula on p. 10 we see that the next step in the calculation of the local sidereal time is to *add* the interval value to the sidereal time for noon G.M.T., because the G.M.T. of birth is *after* noon.

We will recall that we found the sidereal time reading for noon G.M.T. (2H.59M.31S.) by reference to the *1966 Ephemeris*. Peter's birth-date in terms of G.M.T. was the 7th May. All we had to do was to copy the sidereal time figures given for noon against the 7th May (Fig. 3).

We now proceed as follows:

		H.	*M.*	*S.*
Sidereal time noon G.M.T.	=	2	59	31
Interval *TO/FROM noon ＊a.m. –⎱ p.m. +⎰	=	7	52	00
Result	=	10	51	31

As birth is *p.m.* we would put a line through TO and *a.m.*, or we can simply write down:

		H.	*M.*	*S.*
Sidereal time noon G.M.T.	=	2	59	31
Interval FROM noon (+)	=	7	52	00
Result	=	10	51	31

In the first example we are copying the formula as printed on the recommended chart-forms, and by writing this in full at this early stage in learning the calculations the student can note that the interval value is *subtracted* for a birth occurring *before* noon, and *added* for a birth occurring *after* noon. As the interval value for Peter's birth is 7 hours 52 minutes, because birth in G.M.T. was 7.52 p.m., we would delete the TO and the *a.m.* by putting a firm stroke through these. Which tells us that the interval is FROM noon, because birth is *p.m.*, and therefore this value (7 hours 52 minutes) has to be *added* to the noon G.M.T. sidereal time.

However experienced the student may become with regard to natal chart calculations, it cannot be stressed too strongly that he or she must make a habit, when using the printed chart-form, of clearly indicating whether the interval is from the birth-time *to* noon (a.m. birth), or is *from* noon to birth-time (p.m. birth). If no indication is given it is all too easy to subtract the interval value when it should be added, or vice versa. A careless mistake of this nature that goes unnoticed could not only result in the wrong Ascendant and house-positioning of planets, but may waste hours of interpretation work based on wrong figures.

When 24 hours are "Borrowed"

It can often happen that the interval value, that has to be subtracted for a morning birth, is *greater* than the sidereal time at noon G.M.T. This can puzzle the beginner-student, who wonders how a *greater* number can be subtracted from a *lesser* number.

Here is an example. We will assume that birth is 4.28 a.m. G.M.T. on the 7th May 1966, London. Subtracting 4H.28M. from 12H.00M. (noon-time) gives an interval value of 7H.32M. This has to be subtracted from sidereal time at noon G.M.T. on the 7th May. This sidereal time is 2H.59M.31S. This is what we would write down:

		H.	*M.*	*S.*
Sidereal time noon G.M.T.	=	2	59	31
Interval TO noon (a.m. −)	=	7	32	00
Result	=	19	27	31

How did we arrive at *19 hours*?

First we deal with the *seconds*. Interval value in this example case has *no* seconds, so we bring down the 31 seconds shown in the top line. Next we subtract 32 minutes from 59 minutes. Answer = 27 minutes. Now we have to subtract 7 hours from 2 hours. Yet 7 cannot be subtracted from 2. So what we do is *borrow 24 hours*, and add these to the 2 hours *in the top line*. Thus, 24 + 2 = 26 hours.

Why borrow *24* hours? Because there are 24 sidereal hours in one sidereal day.

We can now quite simply subtract 7 hours from a greater number of hours, 26, which gives a result of *19* hours.

When Hours Exceed 24

It sometimes happens that when birth-time G.M.T. is *p.m.*, and therefore the interval value is *added* to sidereal time at noon G.M.T., the result gives a number of hours in excess of 24. This may puzzle some students, because they know that as soon as sidereal hours reach a maximum of *24*, then the sidereal time reading recommences at 0.00 hours. The problem is, what should be done about this? Is the correct procedure to immediately subtract 24 hours from the number that exceeds 24?

Here is an example, in which we give birth-time as 11.21 p.m. G.M.T.

	H.	M.	S.
Sidereal time noon G.M.T. =	22	12	03
Interval FROM noon (p.m. +) =	11	21	
Result =	33	33	03

Should we immediately subtract 24 hours from 33 hours, making the result 9H.33M.03S.? No. We continue with this excess number of hours, and when local sidereal time at birth has been calculated and if the number of hours still exceed 24 we will then make the necessary adjustment (see Chapter 8).

Exercises

The answers to these exercises can be found in Appendix VII.

What is the interval value for the following birth-times? All times are in G.M.T.

18. 0.05 p.m.
19. 0.05 a.m.
20. 3.43 p.m.
21. 3.43 a.m.
22. 6.00 p.m.
23. 6.00 a.m.
24. 9.27 p.m.
25. 9.27 a.m.
26. 0.00 p.m. (noon).
27. 0.00 a.m. (midnight beginning of day).

Sidereal time at noon G.M.T. is given as 2H.59M.31S. What is the *result* when the interval value for each of the following birth-times is applied to this sidereal time, according to the formula for *Step 2* of *Stage 2* in the calculation of local sidereal time at birth (as given on p. 10)?

28. 2.28 p.m. G.M.T.
29. 2.28 a.m. G.M.T.
30. 11.47 p.m. G.M.T.
31. 11.47 a.m. G.M.T.
32. 9.01 a.m. G.M.T.

Sidereal time at noon G.M.T. is given as 18H.22M.15S. What is the *result* when the interval value for each of the following birth-times is applied to this sidereal time, according to the formula for *Step 2* of *Stage 2* in the calculation of local sidereal time at birth (as given on p. 10)?

33. 9.41 p.m. G.M.T.
34. 2.30 a.m. G.M.T.
35. 11.53 p.m. G.M.T.
36. 7.00 p.m. G.M.T.

6 *Finding Local Sidereal Time (3)*

Step 3—Acceleration on Interval

We will refer once again to the formulae given on p. 10. After the *interval value* has been subtracted (if birth G.M.T. is *a.m.*) or added (if birth G.M.T. is *p.m.*) there is a further calculation to be made involving the interval value. This next calculation is *Step 3* in finding the local *sidereal* time at birth. It is known as the *acceleration on the interval*.

This is a necessary adjustment because we are converting *mean time* into *sidereal time*. To emphasize this point the word *sidereal* has been printed in italics in the previous paragraph. A sidereal day[1] is completed *faster* than is a mean (solar) day, by a matter of 3 minutes 55·9 seconds of mean time; or we can see this difference as 24 hours of sidereal time correspond to 23 hours 56 minutes 4·1 seconds of mean time; or, 24 hours of mean time correspond to 24 hours 3 minutes 56·6 seconds of sidereal time.

We can now see why we speak of an *acceleration* by sidereal time on mean time.

Calculating the Acceleration Approximately

Since the interval value can never be more than 12 hours (that is, when birth is either 0.00 a.m. G.M.T. at the beginning of the day, or 0.00 p.m. G.M.T. at noon) which is equal to an acceleration in sidereal time of a mere 1 minute 58 seconds, I suggest that when the student is practised and competent at natal calculations he uses the following formula for quickness:

Acceleration on 1 hour of mean time = 10 seconds of sidereal time.

[1] See *The Astrologer's Astronomical Handbook*, Chapter 7.

Acceleration on 6 minutes of mean time = 1 second of sidereal time.

The way to apply this formula is:

(a) *Multiply* each *hour* of the interval value by *10*, and call the result *seconds*.

(b) *Divide* the *minutes* of the interval value by *6*, and call the result *seconds*.

(c) Add the product of (a) to the quotient of (b). The sum will be *seconds* of sidereal time; or *minutes and seconds* when the sum exceeds 60 seconds.

As an example we will find the sidereal time acceleration on the interval value for Peter's chart. In the previous chapter we found the interval value to be 7 hours 52 minutes.

Referring to (a) in the above formula we first have to *multiply* each *hour* of the interval value by *10*, and call the result seconds of sidereal time. The interval value contains 7 hours. Thus, 7 (hours) × 10 = 70 seconds.

Referring to (b) we have to *divide* the *minutes* of the interval value by *6*, and call the result seconds of sidereal time. The interval value contains 52 minutes. Thus, 52 (minutes) ÷ 6 = 8·6 seconds. As follows:

$$
\begin{array}{r}
8\cdot6 \\
\hline
6)\overline{52} \\
48 \\
\hline
40 \\
36 \\
\hline
4
\end{array}
$$

When the fraction is ·5 or over, convert to one whole second; when less then ·5, ignore the fraction. And so for our example that we calculated as 8·6 seconds, we will call this 9 seconds.

Referring to (c) we have to *add* the product of (a) to the quotient of (b). This is simple:

> (a) = 70 seconds (sidereal time).
> (b) =   9 seconds (sidereal time).
>
> (c) = ‾79 seconds (sidereal time).

The total seconds exceed 60. Therefore we say that 60 seconds = 1 minute. As we have converted 60 seconds into 1 minute we must subtract 60 from the total of 79 seconds, which leaves 19 seconds. Thus, the sidereal time acceleration on the interval value of 7 hours 52 minutes = 79 seconds, or 1 minute 19 seconds.

Most students will quickly find this to be a simple calculation to do and to remember.

As an exercise we will do another quick calculation together.

We will assume that the interval value for a given birth is 9 hours 20 minutes (mean time). See if you can follow each step:

> (a) 9 (hours) × 10 = 90 seconds (sidereal time).
> (b) 20 (minutes) ÷ 6 = 3 seconds (sidereal time).
> (c) (a) = 90 seconds.
>   (b) =   3 seconds.
>
>   (c) = ‾93 seconds, or 1 minute 33 seconds.

Acceleration (sidereal time) on interval = 1 minute 33 seconds.

Calculating the Acceleration Exactly

If precision is needed, or the student prefers or finds it easier to refer to a table of "ready-made" calculations, an *Acceleration Table* is given in Appendix I. This table gives the corresponding sidereal time acceleration on each hour of mean time (0–12 hours) and on each minute of mean time (0–59 minutes).

This is how we use the *Acceleration Table*.

There are only three steps to be taken in the calculation of the acceleration on a given interval value:

(a) Find the sidereal time acceleration corresponding to the number of *hours* of interval value.

(b) Find the sidereal time acceleration corresponding to the number of *minutes* of interval value.

(c) Add (a) and (b). The answer will be seconds, or minutes and seconds of sidereal time.

We will again use Peter's chart as an example. The interval value is 7 hours 52 minutes. Referring to the *Acceleration Table* (Appendix I) we look first for the corresponding sidereal time acceleration to *7 hours* in Table A. The left-hand column gives hours from 0 to 12 in terms of *mean time*. The right-hand column gives the corresponding *sidereal time* acceleration. Running our finger down the left-hand column (hours) we stop at "7". Against this figure, in the right-hand column, we read *1 minute 9·0 seconds*.

The second step (b) is to find the corresponding sidereal time acceleration to *52 minutes* (mean time). We refer now to the column of *minutes* headed *mean time* in Table B. Minutes are given from 0 to 59, and in the right-hand column will be found the corresponding sidereal time acceleration. Running our finger down the left-hand column until we come to *52* (minutes), we read against this in the right-hand column an acceleration of *8·5 seconds*.

The third step (c) is to add the answers for (a) and (b):

$$
\begin{array}{ccc}
 & M. & S. \\
(a) = & 1 & 9\cdot0 \\
(b) = & & 8\cdot5 \\
\hline
(c) = & 1 & 17\cdot5
\end{array}
$$

As we have already stated, when the fraction of a second is ·5 or over we call this one whole second. Therefore the exact calculation (to nearest second) of the sidereal time acceleration on the interval value for Peter's chart is:

1 minute 18 seconds.

It will be seen that there is a difference of *one* second between the answers we arrived at by the two methods of calculation:

Acceleration (approx. calculation) = 1 minute 19 seconds
Acceleration (exact calculation)   = 1 minute 18 seconds

difference =   1 second

A mere discrepancy of one second is of no consequence in the calculation of the local sidereal time at birth, and so it can be left to the individual student to choose his or her own preference of the two methods for finding the acceleration on the interval value.

It should be added at this point, however, that even if split-hair accuracy is not essential in natal chart calculation so far as the ultimate interpretation of the basic figures are concerned (particularly as the birth-time or the co-ordinates of the birthplace are rarely known *exactly*) it *is* essential that the student *learns how to be accurate and conscientious in his calculation of the available birth-data*.

We will use another example interval value, so that you can test how well you have understood how to use the *Acceleration Table*. We will assume that the interval value is *11 hours 19 minutes*.

(*a*) 11 hours (mean time) = 1 minute 48·4 seconds (sidereal time).
(*b*) 19 minutes (mean time) = 3·1 seconds (sidereal time).
(*c*) (*a*) = 1M.48·4S.
    (*b*) =   3·1S.

    (*c*) = 1M.51·5S.

Calling the fraction (·5 seconds) one whole second, we find that the acceleration on the interval value is 1 minute 52 seconds of sidereal time.

Are Seconds of Mean Time to be Ignored?

On rare occasions—usually in the case of an uncertain birth-moment that has been rectified to a speculative time of birth—the birth-time is given in hours, minutes, *and* seconds. This is really quite absurd to bother with mere *seconds* in mean time. Nobody's birth, particularly when it is a speculative time, can be recorded with certainty to a fraction of a minute. In the case of an actual event—the start of a race, the launching of a ship, the moment when a victim's watch stopped as the result of an accident—there may seem to be more justification for calculating a chart to the given fraction of a minute. Yet, even so, no astrologer is going to differentiate in his interpretation of the chart between a planet's position at, say, 9H.21M.15S. p.m. G.M.T., and its position if calculated for (preferably) 9.21 p.m. G.M.T.! Not even if the addition of the 15 seconds brought a new zodiacal sign on to the Ascendant.

My advice is to ignore seconds of *mean time*, or if they are 30 seconds or over to call these one whole minute.

Certainly it would be pointless to try to find the sidereal time acceleration on a given number of seconds of mean time, when one considers that precise acceleration on 1 minute (or 60 seconds) of mean time is 0·16 seconds!

Important Reminder: Is Birth a.m. or p.m.?

The beginner-student cannot be too often reminded to be methodical in his calculations, by stating clearly on the chart-form whether the birth-moment *in G.M.T.* is *before* noon (*a.m.*) or *after* noon (*p.m.*).

If the charts recommended in Appendix III are used the correct procedure is easy to follow, and the risk of careless mistakes is practically eliminated. Referring to page 10 we can see that in Step 2 and Step 3 we would methodically delete TO noon, and *a.m.* –, for the reason that in this case birth in G.M.T. is p.m.

In the previous chapter we learned that when birth is *a.m.* the interval value (from birth *to* noon) is *subtracted* from the sidereal time at noon G.M.T.; when birth is *p.m.* the interval value (*from* noon to birth) is *added* to the sidereal time at noon G.M.T.

Exactly the same procedure applies for the *acceleration* on the interval:

(*a*) If birth G.M.T. is *a.m.*, acceleration on interval is *subtracted*.

(*b*) If birth G.M.T. is *p.m.*, acceleration on interval is *added*.

In this present chapter we have calculated the acceleration on the interval value for Peter's chart to be *1 minute 18 seconds*. This was Step 3 in the calculation of local sidereal time at birth, and if you turn again to the calculations on page 10 you will recognize the most recent calculations we have done, as follows:

		H.	*M.*	*S.*
Result (of Step 2)	=	10	51	31
Step 3. Acceleration on interval (p.m. +)	=		1	18
Sidereal time at Greenwich at birth	=	10	52	49

Exercises

The answers to these exercises can be found in Appendix VII.

What is the acceleration on the following interval values, using the *approximate* method of calculation?

37.   2 hours 22 minutes.
38.   0 hours 38 minutes.
39.   7 hours   0 minutes.

40. 10 hours 10 minutes.
41. 11 hours 59 minutes.
42. 9 hours 12 minutes.
43. 8 hours 2 minutes.
44. 6 hours 44 minutes.
45. 5 hours 55 minutes.
46. 1 hour 41 minutes.

What is the acceleration on the same interval values using the *Acceleration Table* (Appendix I)? Give the answer to fraction of a second, and also the answer to nearest second.

47. 2 hours 22 minutes.
48. 0 hours 38 minutes.
49. 7 hours 0 minutes.
50. 10 hours 10 minutes.
51. 11 hours 59 minutes.
52. 9 hours 12 minutes.
53. 8 hours 2 minutes.
54. 6 hours 44 minutes.
55. 5 hours 55 minutes.
56. 1 hour 41 minutes.

In the following four exercises you will test what you have learned in Chapters 3–6. You must find what is the corresponding Greenwich Mean Time, Greenwich Mean Time date, sidereal time at noon G.M.T., interval value, acceleration on the interval, and sidereal time at Greenwich at birth. The answer you are asked to give for each exercise is the figures for the sidereal time at Greenwich at birth.

57. A birth at 7.53 a.m. B.S.T., 11th May 1966, London.
58. A birth at 6.22 p.m. B.S.T., 22nd May 1966, London.
59. A birth at 9.50 a.m. D.S.T., 12th May 1966, New York, U.S.A. (Long. 74° W.). D.S.T. means that Daylight Saving Time is operating, 1 hour in advance

of E.S.T. Zone Standard Time 5 hours slow on G.M.T.

60. A birth at 0.00 p.m. B.S.T. (noon), 2nd May 1966, London.

The *Acceleration Table* should be used for these four exercises.

7 Finding Local Sidereal Time (4)

Step 4—Longitude Equivalent in Time

The fourth step we have to learn about in the calculation of local sidereal time at birth is what is known as the *longitude equivalent in time*. This refers to the difference in *time* between the place of birth and the Greenwich meridian, determined by their *difference in terrestrial longitude*.

The reason this step has to be taken is this. You have already learned that if the given birth-time is not in Greenwich Mean Time (G.M.T.) we need to convert this to G.M.T. to enable us to use the planets' positions and the sidereal time given in an ephemeris that is *based on G.M.T.* After we have found the corresponding G.M.T. to the given birth-time we have to find what is the local sidereal time for the meridian of the birthplace, so that we can use the *Tables of Houses* for the latitude of the birthplace.

The key figures to enable local sidereal time at birth to be calculated are the hours, minutes and seconds of sidereal time given for noon G.M.T. for the G.M.T. date that one is using. This you were shown how to find and to understand in Chapter 4. Then in Chapters 5 and 6 you learned the next steps, that of finding what is the (*local*) *sidereal time at Greenwich* corresponding to the G.M.T. for birth. For instance, on page 52 we calculated the sidereal time at Greenwich corresponding to the G.M.T. of Peter's birth as 10H.52M.49S. But this is the (local) sidereal time for the Greenwich meridian, not for Peter's birthplace, Oxford. To find what is the local sidereal time *for the Oxford meridian* we have to calculate the *difference in time*, that is mean solar time, between the meridian of Greenwich and the meridian of Oxford, and apply this difference to the sidereal time at Greenwich at birth.

In 1884 the longitude of Greenwich in England was internationally chosen to be longitude 0°, the prime meridian of the world. All places throughout the world that are situated on the same meridian of longitude (0°) as Greenwich have the same local (mean solar) time. For instance, if it is 6 p.m. local time at Greenwich (that is, 6 p.m. Greenwich Mean Time) it will also be 6 p.m. local time for other towns and villages situated on longitude 0° in England, France, Spain, Ghana—whichever country longitude 0° passes through.

But for all other places *not* on the Greenwich meridian the local time will differ from Greenwich local (or mean) time according to their distance apart in terms of terrestrial longitude.

It is quite simple to find what is the difference in local (mean solar) time for any longitude on the Earth's surface and a given Greenwich Mean Time. All one needs to do is multiply by 4 each degree of longitude that the place is east or west of the Greenwich meridian, and call the answer minutes of mean (solar) time.

Why multiply by 4?

Because:

(a) There are 360° of longitude (i.e. 0°–180° eastwards from the Prime Meridian plus 0°–180° westwards = 360°).

(b) The Earth rotates once in 24 hours.

(c) If the Earth rotates once in 24 hours this implies that it turns through:

360° of longitude in 24 hours.

15° of longitude in 1 hour ($360 \div 24 = 15$) or 60 minutes.

1° of longitude in 4 minutes ($60 \div 15 = 4$).

15′ of longitude in 1 minute (60 ÷ 4 = 15).
1′ of longitude in 4 seconds (60 ÷ 4 = 15).

There is an important rule for the student to remember concerning longitude equivalent in time:

(a) If birthplace longitude is *east* of Greenwich, the equivalent time must be *added*.
(b) If birthplace longitude is *west* of Greenwich, the equivalent time must be *subtracted*.

The reason for this is that as the Earth rotates on its axis from *west to east,* a meridian *east* of Greenwich will be transited by the (mean) Sun earlier than it transits the Greenwich meridian. We can understand this more clearly by remembering that the Sun *rises* in the east and *sets* in the west. Because the Sun appears to move slowly against the background of stars compared to the speed of the rotating Earth, the Earth's spinning motion from west to east gives the illusion of the Sun moving in the opposite direction, from east to west. Similarly at night-time the distant stars, the planets, and the Moon, appear to move in a clockwise direction from east to west.

Therefore, when we say that the longitude equivalent in time for a place *east* of Greenwich has to be *added* to Greenwich Mean Time to give the corresponding local (mean) time for that more easterly meridian, we are saying that local (mean) time for places *east* of Greenwich will be in *advance* of Greenwich Mean (or local) Time. Local (mean) time for places *west* of Greenwich will be *slow* of or *behind* Greenwich Mean Time.

As an example, Manchester in England has a longitude of 2° 15′ *west*. This means that the meridian of Manchester is 2° 15′ west of the Greenwich meridian. Our calculations for finding the longitude equivalent in time will look like this:

1° of longitude is equivalent to 4 minutes (mean time).

2° of longitude are therefore equivalent to $2 \times 4 = 8$ minutes (mean time).

15′ of longitude are equivalent to 1 minute (mean time).

Thus:

$$2° \quad = \quad 8 \text{ minutes (mean time)}$$
$$15′ \quad = \quad 1 \text{ minute (mean time)} \Big\} \text{ add}$$
$$\overline{2° \ 15′ \quad = \quad 9 \text{ minutes (mean time)}.}$$

The difference between the longitude of Manchester (2° 15′) and the longitude of Greenwich (0°) when expressed in mean (solar) time is 9 minutes. If, for instance, the time is noon at Greenwich, local time at Manchester will be 11.51 a.m. This is determined by the simple subtraction of 9 minutes from 12.00 noon, because the rule says that *if birthplace longitude is* WEST *of Greenwich, the equivalent time must be* SUBTRACTED.

As another example, the longitude of Stuttgart in Germany is 9° 10′ *east* of Greenwich. Our calculations will look like this:

1° of longitude is equivalent to 4 minutes (mean time).
9° of longitude are therefore equivalent to $9 \times 4 = 36$ minutes (mean time).
1′ of longitude is equivalent to 4 seconds (mean time).
10′ of longitude are therefore equivalent to $10 \times 4 = 40$ seconds (mean time).

Thus:

$$9° \quad = \quad 36 \text{ minutes } 00 \text{ seconds (mean time)}$$
$$10′ \quad = \quad \phantom{36 \text{ minutes } 0} 40 \text{ seconds (mean time)} \Big\} \text{ add}$$
$$\overline{9° \ 10′ \quad = \quad 36 \text{ minutes } 40 \text{ seconds (mean time)}.}$$

The difference between the longitude of Stuttgart (9° 10′) and the longitude of Greenwich (0°) when expressed in mean (solar) time is 36 minutes 40 seconds. If, for example, the time is noon at Greenwich, local time at Stuttgart will be OH.36M.40S. p.m. As the meridian of Stuttgart is *east* of Greenwich the local time for the Stuttgart meridian is arrived at by *adding* the longitude equivalent in time to the G.M.T. Thus:

		H.	M.	S.	
Local time, Greenwich meridian	=	0	00	00	p.m. (noon)
Longitude equivalent in time (east +)	=	0	36	40	
Corresponding local time, Stuttgart	=	0	36	40	p.m.

Tables for Longitude Equivalent in Time

Most students will probably find it quicker and simpler when finding the longitude equivalent in time to refer to the tables given in Appendix II.

The tables are in two parts, *Table A* and *Table B*.

If you turn to Appendix II you will be able to follow my explanation of the two tables.

Table A. In this table the *degrees* of terrestrial longitude are converted into equivalent *hours* and *minutes* of mean (solar) time. You will note there are three columns of figures. The first column is headed with the degrees symbol (°). Degrees are given from 1° to 180°. As there are 360° in a complete circle some students may wonder why only the first 180° are covered by *Table A*. The astrologer will not need to refer to the degrees from 181°–360° because the terrestrial longitudes of places on the Earth's surface are only measured up to 180° east or west from the Prime Meridian at Greenwich (0°). Actually a place that is said to be 180° from the Greenwich meridian could be either east or west of that Prime Meridian. Preferably, I assume, one would simply call the longitude 180°.

The second column in *Table A* is headed *H*. (hours of

mean time), and the third column is headed *M.* (minutes of mean time).

Table B. In this table *minutes* of terrestrial longitude are converted into equivalent *minutes* and *seconds* of mean (solar) time. There are three columns of figures. The first column is headed with the symbol for *minute* or *minutes* (′), and minutes are given from 0′ to 59′. The second column is headed *M.* (minutes of mean time); the third column is headed *S.* (seconds of mean time).

We will give a couple of examples of finding longitude equivalent in time with the use of *Table A* and *Table B*.

Example 1. The terrestrial longitude for Johannesburg in South Africa is given as 28° 8′ E. What is the equivalent mean time?

Referring to *Table A* we run our finger down the first column (degrees) until we come to 28°. Alongside 28°, in the second column, we read *1* (meaning *hour*), and in the third column we read *52* (meaning *minutes*). We have found that 28° of longitude correspond to 1 hour 52 minutes of mean (solar) time.

Next we refer to *Table B,* to find the corresponding *time* to 8′ of longitude. Running our finger down the first column until we come to *8* (minutes of longitude) we will read alongside in the second column the figure *0* (minutes of mean time), and in the third column the figures *32* (seconds of mean time). We have found that 8′ of longitude correspond to 0 minutes 32 seconds of mean (solar) time.

All we have left to do is add together the mean time readings from *Table A* and *Table B*, as follows:

		H.	M.	S.
28° of longitude	=	1	52	00
8′ of longitude	=			32
28° 8′ of longitude	=	1	52	32

Example 2. See if you can find the same measures of

mean (solar) time corresponding to the terrestrial longitude 109° 50′ W. for Lowell in Arizona, U.S.A. Here are my figures:

		H.	M.	S.
109° of longitude	=	7	16	00
50′ of longitude	=		3	20
109° 50′ of longitude	=	7	19	20

Peter's Chart: Longitude Equivalent in Time

Now that we have explained all that the student needs to know about *longitude equivalent in time*, we can make the final step in the calculation of the local sidereal time at birth for our example birth, Peter.

This is already calculated for us on page 10, as *Step 4*. Peter was born in Oxford, England. The meridian (of longitude) for Oxford is 1° 15′ *west* of the Greenwich meridian (0°). As Oxford is *west* of Greenwich we carefully delete "E +" given against Step 4. This leaves "W –", telling us quite clearly that the longitude equivalent in time must be *subtracted* from the sidereal time at Greenwich at birth. We must now find the equivalent time to 1° 15′ of terrestrial longitude. Referring to *Table A* and *Table B* in Appendix II this is what we shall find:

		H.	M.	S.
1° of longitude	=		4	00 (mean time)
15′ of longitude	=		1	00 (mean time)
1° 15′ of longitude	=		5	00 (mean time)

We can now make the final step in c lculating local sidereal time at Peter's birth.

		H.	M.	S.
Sid. time at Greenwich at birth	=	10	52	49

Step 4: Longitude equivalent in time

$$(W-) = \qquad 5 \quad 00$$

Local sidereal time at birth $= \quad 10 \quad 47 \quad 49$

Before we learn what we have to do with the local sidereal time at birth of 10 hours 47 minutes 49 seconds, to enable us to find the Ascendant, Midheaven, and house cusps for Peter's natal chart, we will learn what adjustment has to be made when the local sidereal time at birth *exceeds* 24 hours. This will be explained in Chapter 8.

Exercises

You can now test yourself to find whether you have understood what you have read in this chapter. The answers to these exercises can be found in Appendix VII.

Two answers (*a*) and (*b*) must be given to each of the following exercises.

(*a*) What is the *longitude equivalent in time* for the following longitudes?

(*b*) In each case, local sidereal time at Greenwich is 22H.41M.28S. By subtracting or adding (whichever applies in each case) the longitude equivalent in time, what is the *local sidereal time at birth?*

61. Fairchild, U.S.A., longitude 90° 58′ west.
62. Anadyr, U.S.S.R., longitude 178′ 0′ east.
63. Welwyn, England, longitude 0° 11′ west.
64. Seattle, U.S.A., longitude 122° 20′ west.
65. Genoa, Italy, longitude 8° 57′ east.

8 When L.S.T. at Birth Exceeds 24 Hours

It frequently happens that the local sidereal time at birth (L.S.T.) exceeds 24 hours.

All that one has to do in such a case is to subtract *one whole day of 24 hours* from the local sidereal time at birth. Example:

A birth occurs in Glasgow, Scotland (Lat. 55° 52′ N.; Long. 4° 7′ W.) on the 12th March 1944, at 10.25 p.m. G.M.T.

		H.	M.	S.
Sidereal time noon G.M.T.	=	23	20	02
Interval from noon (p.m. +)	=	10	25	00
Result =		33	45	02
Acceleration on interval (p.m. +) =			1	43
Sidereal time at Greenwich at birth	=	33	46	45
Longitude equivalent in time (W −) =			16	28
Local sidereal time at birth	=	33	30	17
Subtract 24 hours		24		
Local sidereal time at birth	=	9	30	17

The reason, of course, why 24 hours has to be subtracted in a case like this is because a sidereal day is reckoned from 0–24 hours. Sidereal time given in the *Tables of Houses*, to which the local sidereal time at birth has to be applied if we are to know what are the corresponding Ascendant and Midheaven, is therefore only reckoned from 0–24 hours.

When 48 Hours are Subtracted

Sometimes the local sidereal time at birth exceeds *48* hours. In this case we must subtract *48* hours from the local sidereal time at birth to give us the correct reading that must be within the limits of 24 hours.

Example:

A birth occurs in Sydney, Australia (Lat. 33° 53′ S.; Long. 151° 10′ E.), and when birth-time is converted into the corresponding G.M.T. the data is:

> G.M.T. date: 12th March 1944
> G.M.T.:   10.25 p.m.

		H.	*M.*	*S.*
Sidereal time noon G.M.T.	=	23	20	02
Interval from noon (p.m. +)	=	10	25	00
Result	=	33	45	02
Acceleration on interval (p.m. +)	=		1	43
Sidereal time at Greenwich at birth	=	33	46	45
Longitude equivalent in time (E +)	=	10	04	40
Local sidereal time at birth, if birth were in North Hemisphere	=	43	51	25
Add 12 hours, because birth occurs in Southern Hemisphere	=	12		
		55	51	25
Subtract 48 hours		48		
Local sidereal time at birth	=	7	51	25

In the above example the student will note that as soon as the interval value (10H.25M.) is added to sidereal time noon G.M.T. the figures in the *hours column* exceed 24 by 9 hours (to 33 hours). But we do not subtract 24 hours from this excess figure yet. Not until the local sidereal time at birth has been calculated. This is simply because it is best to complete the calculations first, as it can happen that, for instance, a figure in excess of 24 hours is reduced to less than 24 again when the longitude equivalent in time is subtracted (when birthplace is west of Greenwich). If we had prematurely subtracted 24 hours before this stage, we may well find that the number of hours left over would be less than the longitude equivalent in time—which would mean borrowing those same 24 hours again!

This will be made clear with an example:

A birth occurs in San Francisco, U.S.A. (Lat. 37° 35′ N.; Long. 122° 30′ W.), where the birth-time after conversion to G.M.T. is 7.40 p.m. on the 12th March 1944.

		H.	*M.*	*S.*
Sidereal time noon G.M.T.	=	23	20	02
Interval from noon (p.m. +)	=	7	40	00
Result	=	31	00	02
Acceleration on interval (p.m. +)	=		1	16
Sidereal time at Greenwich at birth	=	31	01	18
We decide to subtract 24 hours		24		
		7	01	18
Longitude equivalent in time (W –)	=	8	10	00

You can see what has happened, we now have to subtract a greater number from a lesser number, which means mentally adding 24 hours to the lesser number so that 8 hours can be subtracted. And so the point made is that it is best not to start subtracting 24 hours until this is found to be necessary after local sidereal time at birth has been calculated.

The student will soon take in his stride this kind of adjustment in chart calculation. To have to *think* whether or not to subtract 24 or 48 hours may at this early stage seem just another complication (to what is to many astrologers and students a very boring and tedious part of astrology—the wretched calculations!). But with perseverance and the sustained enthusiasm to learn *every side* of the basic essentials of astrology, the conscientious student will probably be surprised—and delighted—how quickly he or she masters the calculations and so finds them to be quite simple after all.

9 *Finding the Angles in Tables of Houses*

In Chapters 4–7 we learnt how to calculate the local sidereal time at birth. Our next step is to know how to use this local sidereal time to find the corresponding Ascendant, M.C., and house cusps.

The Ascendant and M.C. are the two most important points determining the *angles* (Fig. 1) of an individual birth-chart. It is the relationship of the angles to the zodiacal signs and the planetary pattern existing at the moment of birth which makes the chart *personal* and unique, distinct from the charts of each other person born on the same day and in different localities. When the time of birth is unknown, or is uncertain, the local sidereal time at birth and the angles of the chart can never be known for sure.

In this chapter you will learn how to find the *approximate* longitude reading for the Ascendant and M.C. by reference to *Tables of Houses*. In Chapter 10 you can learn how to calculate the *exact* Ascendant and M.C.

Using the Tables of Houses

The *Tables of Houses* are published tables covering various latitudes from the equator towards the poles, for the purpose of finding the Ascendant, Midheaven, and house cusps corresponding to a given local sidereal time at birth. These tables save what would otherwise be a tedious and complicated task if such calculations were not already prepared. It is advisable that the student obtains the two reference books that are recommended in Appendix III:

Raphael's Tables of Houses for Northern Latitudes
Raphael's Tables of Houses for Great Britain

This is the procedure for finding the sign and degree on the Ascendant (1st house cusp), on the Midheaven (M.C.), and on each of the other eleven house cusps:

1. Note what the *local sidereal time at birth* is for the chart you are doing.
2. Open the *Tables of Houses* to the two pages for the *nearest* latitude to the latitude of birthplace.
3. Run your finger down the column headed *Sidereal Time* until you come to a reading (in hours, minutes, and seconds) *nearest* to the local sidereal time at birth.
4. Alongside this *nearest* sidereal time will be found the corresponding signs and degrees of the *Ascendant* and *Midheaven*. These can be entered direct on to the chart-form.
5. For the recommended Equal House System the signs and degrees on the cusps of the second to twelfth houses will easily be found by adding *exactly 30°* to the Ascendant (1st house cusp) which will give the second house cusp; and adding 30° to the second house cusp which will give the third house cusp, and so on. The twelve houses will be, as the name of the house system implies, of *equal* 30° size.

Fig. 5 shows what the first of the two pages of tables for latitude 51° 32′ north looks like. The first page covers sidereal time 0H.00M.00S. to 12H.00M.00S. Fig. 6 shows the second page of tables for the same latitude and covering sidereal time 12H.00M.00S. to 24H.00M.00S. Sidereal time 24H.00M.00S. is another way of saying 0H.00M.00S. This is because one sidereal day comprises 24 hours. An exact reading of 24 hours completes one cycle and also begins a new cycle. The student will see that the same

TABLES OF HOUSES FOR LONDON, Latitude 51° 32′ N.

Sidereal Time (H. M. S.)	10 ♈	11 ♉	12 ♊	Ascen ♋	2 ♌	3 ♍
0 0 0	0	9	22	26 36	12	3
0 3 40	1	10	23	27 17	13	3
0 7 20	2	11	24	27 56	14	4
0 11 0	3	12	25	28 42	15	5
0 14 41	4	13	25	29 17	15	6
0 18 21	5	14	26	29 55	16	7
0 22 2	6	15	27	0 ♌ 34	17	8
0 25 42	7	16	28	1 14	18	8
0 29 23	8	17	29	1 55	18	9
0 33 4	9	18	♋	2 33	19	10
0 36 45	10	19	1	3 14	20	11
0 40 26	11	20	1	3 54	20	12
0 44 8	12	21	2	4 33	21	13
0 47 50	13	22	3	5 12	22	14
0 51 32	14	23	4	5 52	23	15
0 55 14	15	24	5	6 30	23	15
0 58 57	16	25	6	7 9	24	16
1 2 40	17	26	6	7 50	25	17
1 6 23	18	27	7	8 30	26	18
1 10 7	19	28	8	9 9	26	19
1 13 51	20	29	9	9 48	27	19
1 17 35	21	♊	10	10 28	28	20
1 21 20	22	1	10	11 8	28	21
1 25 6	23	2	11	11 48	29	22
1 28 52	24	3	12	12 28	♍	23
1 32 38	25	4	13	13 8	1	24
1 36 25	26	5	14	13 48	1	25
1 40 12	27	6	14	14 28	2	25
1 44 0	28	7	15	15 8	3	26
1 47 48	29	8	16	15 48	4	27
1 51 37	30	9	17	16 28	4	28

Sidereal Time (H. M. S.)	10 ♉	11 ♊	12 ♋	Ascen ♌	2 ♍	3 ♎
1 51 37	0	9	17	16 28	4	28
1 55 27	1	10	18	17 8	5	29
1 59 17	2	11	19	17 48	6	♎
2 3 8	3	12	19	18 28	7	1
2 6 59	4	13	20	19 9	8	2
2 10 51	5	14	21	19 49	9	2
2 14 44	6	15	22	20 29	9	3
2 18 37	7	16	22	21 10	10	4
2 22 31	8	17	23	21 51	11	5
2 26 25	9	18	24	22 32	11	6
2 30 20	10	19	25	23 14	12	7
2 34 16	11	20	25	23 55	13	8
2 38 13	12	21	26	24 36	14	9
2 42 10	13	22	27	25 17	15	10
2 46 8	14	23	28	25 58	15	11
2 50 0	15	24	29	26 40	16	12
2 54 7	16	25	29	27 22	17	12
2 58 7	17	26	♌	28 4	18	13
3 2 8	18	27	1	28 46	18	14
3 6 9	19	27	2	29 28	19	15
3 10 12	20	28	3	0 ♍ 12	20	16
3 14 15	21	29	3	0 54	21	17
3 18 19	22	♋	4	1 36	22	18
3 22 23	23	1	5	2 20	22	19
3 26 29	24	2	6	3 2	23	20
3 30 35	25	3	7	3 45	24	21
3 34 41	26	4	7	4 28	25	22
3 38 49	27	5	8	5 11	26	23
3 42 57	28	6	9	5 54	27	24
3 47 6	29	7	10	6 38	27	25
3 51 15	30	8	11	7 21	28	25

Sidereal Time (H. M. S.)	10 ♊	11 ♋	12 ♌	Ascen ♍	2 ♍	3 ♎
3 51 15	0	8	11	7 21	28	25
3 55 25	1	9	12	8 5	29	26
3 59 36	2	10	12	8 49	♎	27
4 3 48	3	10	13	9 33	1	28
4 8 0	4	11	14	10 17	2	29
4 12 13	5	12	15	11 2	2	♏
4 16 26	6	13	16	11 46	3	1
4 20 40	7	14	17	12 30	4	2
4 24 55	8	15	17	13 15	5	3
4 29 10	9	16	18	14 0	6	4
4 33 26	10	17	19	14 45	7	5
4 37 42	11	18	20	15 30	8	6
4 41 59	12	19	21	16 15	8	7
4 46 16	13	20	21	17 0	9	8
4 50 34	14	21	22	17 45	10	9
4 54 52	15	22	23	18 30	11	10
4 59 10	16	23	24	19 16	12	11
5 3 29	17	24	25	20 3	13	12
5 7 49	18	25	26	20 49	14	13
5 12 9	19	25	27	21 35	14	14
5 16 29	20	26	28	22 20	15	14
5 20 49	21	27	28	23 6	16	15
5 25 9	22	28	29	23 51	17	16
5 29 30	23	29	♍	24 37	18	17
5 33 51	24	♌	1	25 23	19	18
5 38 12	25	1	2	26 9	20	19
5 42 34	26	2	3	26 55	21	20
5 46 55	27	3	4	27 41	21	21
5 51 17	28	4	4	28 27	22	22
5 55 38	29	5	5	29 13	23	23
6 0 0	30	6	6	30 0	24	24

Sidereal Time (H. M. S.)	10 ♋	11 ♌	12 ♍	Ascen ♎	2 ♎	3 ♏
6 0 0	0	6	6	0 ♎ 0	24	24
6 4 22	1	7	7	0 47	25	25
6 8 43	2	8	8	1 33	26	26
6 13 5	3	9	9	2 19	27	27
6 17 26	4	10	10	3 5	27	28
6 21 48	5	11	10	3 51	28	29
6 26 9	6	12	11	4 37	29	♏
6 30 30	7	13	12	5 23	♏	1
6 34 51	8	14	13	6 9	1	2
6 39 11	9	15	14	6 55	2	3
6 43 31	10	16	15	7 40	2	4
6 47 51	11	16	16	8 26	3	4
6 52 11	12	17	16	9 12	4	5
6 56 31	13	18	17	9 58	5	6
7 0 50	14	19	18	10 43	6	7
7 5 8	15	20	19	11 28	7	8
7 9 26	16	21	20	12 14	8	9
7 13 44	17	22	21	12 59	8	10
7 18 1	18	23	22	13 45	9	11
7 22 18	19	24	23	14 30	10	12
7 26 34	20	25	24	15 15	11	13
7 30 50	21	26	25	16 0	12	14
7 35 5	22	27	26	16 45	13	15
7 39 20	23	28	26	17 30	13	16
7 43 34	24	29	27	18 15	14	17
7 47 47	25	♍	28	18 59	15	18
7 52 0	26	1	29	19 43	16	19
7 56 12	27	2	29	20 27	17	20
8 0 24	28	3	♎	21 11	18	20
8 4 35	29	4	1	21 56	18	21
8 8 45	30	5	2	22 40	19	22

Sidereal Time (H. M. S.)	10 ♌	11 ♍	12 ♎	Ascen ♎	2 ♏	3 ♐
8 8 45	0	5	2	22 40	19	22
8 12 54	1	5	3	23 24	20	23
8 17 3	2	6	3	24 7	21	24
8 21 11	3	7	4	24 50	22	25
8 25 19	4	8	5	25 34	23	26
8 29 26	5	9	6	26 18	23	27
8 33 31	6	10	7	27 1	24	28
8 37 37	7	11	8	27 44	25	29
8 41 41	8	12	8	28 26	26	♐
8 45 45	9	13	9	29 9	27	1
8 49 48	10	14	10	29 50	27	2
8 53 51	11	15	11	0 ♏ 31	28	3
8 57 52	12	16	12	1 15	29	4
9 1 53	13	17	12	1 58	♐	4
9 5 53	14	18	13	2 39	1	5
9 9 53	15	18	14	3 21	1	6
9 13 52	16	19	15	4 3	2	7
9 17 50	17	20	16	4 44	3	8
9 21 47	18	21	16	5 26	3	9
9 25 44	19	22	17	6 7	4	10
9 29 40	20	23	18	6 48	5	11
9 33 35	21	24	18	7 29	5	12
9 37 29	22	25	19	8 9	6	13
9 41 23	23	26	20	8 50	7	14
9 45 16	24	27	21	9 31	8	15
9 49 9	25	28	21	10 11	9	16
9 53 1	26	28	22	10 51	9	16
9 56 52	27	29	23	11 32	10	18
10 0 43	28	♎	24	12 11	11	19
10 4 33	29	1	25	12 53	12	20
10 8 23	30	2	26	13 33	13	20

Sidereal Time (H. M. S.)	10 ♍	11 ♎	12 ♏	Ascen ♏	2 ♐	3 ♑
10 8 23	0	2	26	13 33	13	20
10 12 12	1	3	26	14 13	14	21
10 16 0	2	4	27	14 53	15	22
10 19 48	3	5	28	15 33	15	23
10 23 35	4	5	29	16 13	16	24
10 27 22	5	6	29	16 52	17	25
10 31 8	6	7	♏	17 31	18	26
10 34 54	7	8	1	18 12	19	27
10 38 40	8	9	2	18 52	20	27
10 42 25	9	10	2	19 31	20	29
10 46 9	10	11	3	20 11	21	♑
10 49 53	11	11	4	20 50	22	1
10 53 37	12	12	4	21 31	22	2
10 57 20	13	14	5	22 9	24	3
11 1 3	14	14	6	22 49	24	4
11 4 46	15	15	7	23 28	25	5
11 8 28	16	16	7	24 8	26	6
11 12 10	17	17	8	24 47	27	8
11 15 52	18	17	9	25 27	28	9
11 19 34	19	18	10	26 6	29	10
11 23 15	20	19	10	26 45	♑	11
11 26 56	21	20	11	27 25	0	12
11 30 37	22	21	12	28 4	1	13
11 34 18	23	22	13	28 44	2	14
11 37 58	24	23	13	29 24	3	15
11 41 39	25	24	14	0 ♐ 3	4	16
11 45 19	26	25	15	0 43	5	17
11 49 0	27	25	15	1 23	6	18
11 52 40	28	26	16	2 2	6	19
11 56 20	29	27	17	2 43	7	20
12 0 0	30	28	17	3 23	8	21

Fig. 5

© W. Foulsham & Co. Ltd.

TABLES OF HOUSES FOR LONDON, Latitude 51° 32′ N.

Sidereal Time (H. M. S.)	10 ♎	11 ♎	12 ♏	Ascen ♐	2 ♑	3 ♒
12 0 0	0	27	17	3 23	8	21
12 3 40	1	28	18	4 4	9	28
12 7 20	2	29	19	4 45	10	24
12 11 0	3	♏	20	5 26	11	25
12 14 41	4	1	20	6 7	12	26
12 18 21	5	1	21	6 48	13	27
12 22 2	6	2	22	7 29	14	28
12 25 42	7	3	23	8 10	15	29
12 29 23	8	4	23	8 51	16	♓
12 33 4	9	5	24	9 33	17	2
12 36 45	10	6	25	10 15	18	3
12 40 26	11	6	25	10 57	19	4
12 44 8	12	7	26	11 40	20	5
12 47 50	13	8	27	12 22	21	6
12 51 32	14	9	28	13 4	22	7
12 55 14	15	10	28	13 47	23	8
12 58 57	16	11	29	14 30	24	10
13 2 40	17	11	♐	15 14	25	11
13 6 23	18	12	1	15 59	26	12
13 10 7	19	13	1	16 44	27	13
13 13 51	20	14	2	17 29	28	15
13 17 35	21	15	3	18 14	29	16
13 21 20	22	16	4	19 0	♒	17
13 25 6	23	16	4	19 45	1	18
13 28 52	24	17	5	20 31	2	20
13 32 38	25	18	6	21 18	4	21
13 36 25	26	19	7	22 6	5	22
13 40 12	27	20	7	22 54	6	23
13 44 0	28	21	8	23 42	7	25
13 47 48	29	21	9	24 31	8	26
13 51 37	30	22	10	25 20	10	27

Sidereal Time (H. M. S.)	10 ♏	11 ♏	12 ♐	Ascen ♑	2 ♒	3 ♓
13 51 37	0	22	10	25 20	10	27
13 55 27	1	23	11	26 20	11	28
13 59 17	2	24	11	27 2	12	♈
14 3 8	3	25	12	27 53	14	1
14 6 59	4	26	13	28 45	15	2
14 10 51	5	26	14	29 36	16	4
14 14 44	6	27	15	0♑29	18	5
14 18 37	7	28	15	1 23	19	6
14 22 31	8	29	16	2 18	20	8
14 26 25	9	♐	17	3 14	22	9
14 30 20	10	1	18	4 11	23	10
14 34 16	11	2	19	5 9	25	11
14 38 13	12	2	20	6 7	26	13
14 42 10	13	3	20	7 6	28	14
14 46 8	14	4	21	8 6	29	15
14 50 7	15	5	22	9 8	♓	17
14 54 7	16	6	23	10 11	2	18
14 58 7	17	7	24	11 15	4	19
15 2 8	18	8	25	12 20	6	21
15 6 9	19	9	26	13 27	8	22
15 10 12	20	9	27	14 35	9	23
15 14 15	21	10	27	15 43	11	24
15 18 19	22	11	28	16 52	13	26
15 22 23	23	12	29	18 3	14	27
15 26 29	24	13	♑	19 16	16	28
15 30 35	25	14	1	20 32	17	29
15 34 41	26	15	2	21 48	19	♈
15 38 49	27	16	3	23 8	21	1
15 42 57	28	17	4	24 29	22	3
15 47 6	29	18	5	25 51	24	4
15 51 15	30	18	6	27 15	26	6

Sidereal Time (H. M. S.)	10 ♐	11 ♐	12 ♑	Ascen ♒	2 ♓	3 ♈
15 51 15	0	18	6	27 15	26	6
15 55 25	1	19	7	28 42	28	7
15 59 36	2	20	8	0♒11	♈	9
16 3 48	3	21	9	1 42	2	10
16 8 0	4	22	10	3 16	3	11
16 12 13	5	23	11	4 53	5	12
16 16 26	6	24	12	6 32	7	14
16 20 40	7	25	13	8 13	9	15
16 24 55	8	26	14	9 57	11	16
16 29 10	9	27	16	11 44	12	17
16 33 26	10	28	17	13 34	14	18
16 37 42	11	29	18	15 26	16	20
16 41 59	12	♑	19	17 20	18	21
16 46 16	13	1	20	19 17	20	22
16 50 34	14	2	21	21 22	22	23
16 54 52	15	3	22	23 29	23	25
16 59 10	16	4	24	25 46	25	26
17 3 29	17	5	25	27 46	27	27
17 7 49	18	6	26	0♓28	♉	28
17 12 9	19	7	27	2 19	2	29
17 16 31	20	8	28	4 12	4	♉
17 20 49	21	9	29	...	...	...
17 25 9	22	10	♒	...	...	...
17 29 30	23	11	1	...	...	...
17 33 51	24	12	2	...	...	...
17 38 12	25	13	3	...	...	...
17 42 34	26	14	5	...	...	...
17 46 55	27	15	6	...	...	...
17 51 15	28	16	8	...	...	...
17 55 38	29	17	11	...	...	...
18 0 0	0	18	13	0 17	15	...

Sidereal Time (H. M. S.)	10 ♑	11 ♑	12 ♒	Ascen ♈	2 ♉	3 ♊
18 0 0	0	18	13	0 17	11	20
18 4 22	1	20	14	2 39	13	21
18 8 43	2	21	16	5 19	14	22
18 13 5	3	22	17	7 55	16	23
18 17 26	4	23	19	10 29	18	25
18 21 48	5	24	20	13 2	19	26
18 26 9	6	25	22	15 36	21	27
18 30 30	7	26	23	18 6	22	29
18 34 51	8	27	25	20 34	24	♊
18 39 11	9	29	27	22 59	25	1
18 43 31	10	♒	28	25 21	26	2
18 47 51	11	1	♓	27 42	28	3
18 52 11	12	2	2	29 58	♊	4
18 56 31	13	3	3	2♉13	1	5
19 0 50	14	4	5	4 24	3	6
19 5 8	15	6	7	6 30	4	8
19 9 26	16	7	9	8 36	6	9
19 13 44	17	8	10	10 40	7	10
19 18 1	18	9	12	12 39	9	12
19 22 18	19	10	14	14 35	10	13
19 26 34	20	12	16	16 28	12	14
19 30 50	21	13	18	17 14	13	15
19 35 5	22	14	19	20 3	15	16
19 39 20	23	15	21	21 48	17	17
19 43 34	24	16	23	23 29	18	18
19 47 47	25	18	25	25 9	19	21
19 52 0	26	19	27	26 45	20	21
19 56 12	27	20	28	28 18	21	22
20 0 24	28	21	♈	29 49	22	23
20 4 35	29	23	2	1♊19	23	24
20 8 45	30	24	4	2 45	24	12

Sidereal Time (H. M. S.)	10 ♒	11 ♒	12 ♈	Ascen ♊	2 ♊	3 ♋
20 8 45	0	24	4	2 45	24	12
20 12 54	1	25	6	4 9	25	12
20 17 3	2	27	7	5 32	26	13
20 21 11	3	28	9	6 53	27	14
20 25 19	4	29	10	8 12	28	15
20 29 26	5	♓	11	9 26	29	16
20 33 31	6	2	14	10 43	♋	17
20 37 37	7	3	16	11 58	1	18
20 41 41	8	4	18	13 9	2	19
20 45 45	9	6	19	14 11	4	19
20 49 48	10	7	21	15 25	5	20
20 53 51	11	8	23	16 37	6	21
20 57 52	12	9	24	17 44	8	22
21 1 53	13	11	26	18 51	9	23
21 5 53	14	13	29	20 5	11	24
21 9 53	15	13	29	21 13	12	25
21 13 52	16	15	♉	21 52	13	26
21 17 50	17	16	2	22 47	14	27
21 21 47	18	17	4	23 44	16	28
21 25 44	19	19	5	24 50	17	29
21 29 40	20	20	7	25 48	19	♌
21 33 35	21	22	8	26 56	21	1
21 37 29	22	23	10	28 0	22	2
21 41 23	23	24	11	29 8	24	4
21 45 16	24	26	13	0♋15	25	5
21 49 9	25	26	14	9 22	26	0♌
21 52 0	26	27	16	45 20	1	15
21 56 12	27	20	18	18 21	56	52
22 0 24	28	21	♈	29 49	22	10
22 4 35	29	23	2	1♊19	23	11
22 8 23	30	24	2	8 23	30	3

Sidereal Time (H. M. S.)	10 ♓	11 ♈	12 ♉	Ascen ♋	2 ♋	3 ♌
22 8 23	0	3	20	4 38	20	8
22 12 12	1	4	21	5 28	21	8
22 16 0	2	6	23	6 17	22	9
22 19 48	3	7	24	7 5	23	10
22 23 35	4	8	25	7 53	25	11
22 27 22	5	9	26	8 42	24	12
22 31 8	6	10	28	9 29	25	13
22 34 54	7	12	29	10 16	26	14
22 38 40	8	13	♊	11 2	26	14
22 42 57	9	14	1	11 47	27	15
22 46 0	10	15	2	12 31	28	16
22 49 53	11	17	3	13 16	29	17
22 53 37	12	18	4	14 14	♌	19
22 57 20	13	19	5	14 45	1	19
23 1 20	14	20	6	15 28	1	19
23 4 46	15	21	7	16 11	2	20
23 8 28	16	23	8	16 54	2	21
23 12 10	17	25	9	17 37	3	22
23 15 52	18	25	10	18 20	4	23
23 19 26	19	27	11	19 3	5	24
23 23 15	20	27	12	19 45	5	24
23 26 56	21	29	13	20 26	6	25
23 30 37	22	♉	14	21 6	7	26
23 34 18	23	1	15	21 50	7	26
23 37 58	24	2	16	22 31	8	28
23 41 39	25	3	17	12 0♌	9	29
23 45 19	26	4	18	13 53	9	29
23 49 0	27	5	19	24 32	10	♍
23 52 40	28	6	20	25 15	11	1
23 56 0	29	8	21	25 36	13	3
0 0 0	30	9	22	26 36	13	3

Fig. 6

© W. Foulsham & Co. Ltd.

figures are on the house cusps corresponding to 0H.00M. 00S. as those corresponding to 24H.00M.00S.

Each of the two pages reproduced from the *Tables of Houses* are divided into *six* sections. Each section is subdivided into *seven* columns. The *first* column in each section always refers to *sidereal time*, as will be seen from the heading. It is these first columns we refer to as we look for the sidereal time *nearest* to the local sidereal time at birth.

Under the heading *Sidereal Time* in the first column are the letters *H.M.S.* Each letter is at the top of a column of figures. *H.* means *hours; M.* means *minutes; S.* means *seconds.* For example, referring to Fig. 5 and the first section (of six sections) in the top left-hand corner, the sidereal time reading in the second line is "0 3 40". These figures imply 0H.03M.40S., or 0 hours 3 minutes 40 seconds of sidereal time.

The *second* column in each section refers to the zodiacal sign and the degree on the Midheaven (M.C.), corresponding to the sidereal time given in column one. At the top of this column are the numerals *10*, and underneath, a sign of the zodiac. The *10* refers to the *10th house cusp* for the Placidus House System. By Placidus the 10th house cusp is *always* the same sign and degree as the Midheaven. This is *not* the 10th house cusp for the Equal House System, but it *is* the same M.C. for the Equal House and the Placidus Systems.

When celestial longitude measured along the equator from the meridian of a place with latitude 51° 32' north to the First Point of Aries is, for example, 1 hour 10 minutes 7 seconds (1H.10M.07S.), the sign and degree culminating at the M.C. is ♈ 19°. You can check this in Fig. 5. In the first column in the top left-hand section you will find 1H.10M.07S. In the second column (headed *10* and with the Aries symbol ♈ directly underneath) and in line with this sidereal time reading is the number *19*, meaning 19 degrees. As this second column is headed with the ♈ symbol we know that the corresponding degree culminating at the Midheaven is ♈ 19°.

The second column in each of the twelve sections shown in Figs. 5 and 6 contains exactly *thirty* degrees. Actually thirty-one lines of figures are given, but the bottom line in each section is identical to the top line in the following section; except that 30° appears in the second column of the bottom line, whilst 0° is entered in the second column of the top line of the following section.

The reason why there are *twelve* sections of tables for any given latitude is because there are *twelve* zodiacal signs, and the second column in each section as we have seen covers the complete thirty degrees of a particular sign.

Column *three* in each section refers to the sign and the degree on the *eleventh* house cusp according to the Placidus House System. This is indicated by the number *11* heading the column. Whereas the *second* column provides the exact thirty degrees of a sign, the readings for the other Placidus house cusps given in columns three to seven do not cover exactly thirty degrees. This is because these tables are based on sidereal time measurements *for the Midheaven* corresponding to the thirty degrees of each sign; and because some signs take longer to rise at the Ascendant or to cross the cusps of houses.

Referring to column *three* in the first section of the tables in Fig. 5 we may note that directly under the number *11* (11th Placidus house cusp) at the top of the column is the Taurus symbol ♉. In column *two* (headed *10*) the sign Aries (♈) commenced at 0°. In column *three*, however, Taurus begins at 9°. Where are the "missing" degrees? They will be found in the section of tables that directly precedes this first section. So we turn to Fig. 6 and refer to the *twelfth* section (bottom right-hand corner) that commences with sidereal time 22H.08M.23S. and finishes with 24H.00M.00S. In the lower portion of column *three* in this section will be found the symbol for Taurus (♉) corresponding to sidereal time 23H.30M.37S. followed by the numbers 1 to 9 (degrees of longitude).

The 24 hours cycle in sidereal time reckoning is completed at the foot of the twelfth section in Fig. 6, and immediately commences a new cycle corresponding to 0H.00M.00S. at the top of the first section in Fig. 5.

Incidentally, when a new sign begins in columns three, four, six, and seven, the sign's symbol is given. This also corresponds approximately to 0° of that sign, there not being room to include both the sign and the numeral.

Column *four* in each section refers to the sign and the degree on the *twelfth* house Placidus cusp, indicated by *12* heading the column. For example:

Sidereal time 0H.00M.00S. gives 12th house cusp ♊ 22°
Sidereal time 3H.47M.06S. gives 12th house cusp ♌ 10°
Sidereal time 21H.09M.53S. gives 12th house cusp ♈ 29°

Column *five* in each section is of special significance whatever the house system used. This column gives the sign, degree (°) and minute (′) on the *Ascendant* or first house cusp corresponding to a given sidereal time. This is indicated at the top of the column by the abbreviation *Ascen*. Directly underneath is the Rising Sign. As the Ascendant is one of the angles it is more accurately calculated than for the other Placidus house cusps.

A very important point to remember when extracting signs and degrees from the *Tables of Houses* is to be sure that you have the *correct sign*. Be careful not to automatically "read off" the sign shown at the *top* of a column, without noting first whether the sign has *changed* by the time the degree corresponding to the sidereal time you are using has been reached. For example, we are finding the Ascendant corresponding to 9H.37M.29S. sidereal time. We find this in the *fifth section* of the tables (Fig. 5), and note the figures, 8° 9′. If we are careless we look at the sign given at the *top* of the fifth column. It is ♎ (Libra). So we enter the Ascendant on the chart-form as ♎ 8° 9′. But we are wrong! Part way down the fifth column in section five the ascending sign *changes*, to Scorpio (♏). The correct Ascendant should be ♏ 8° 9′.

Column *six* in each section refers to the sign and the degree on the Placidus *second* house cusp, as indicated by the figure *2* heading the column.

Column *seven* in each section refers to the sign and the degree on the *third* house cusp (Placidus), as shown by the figure *3* heading the column.

Finding the Fourth to Ninth House Cusps

We have seen how to find the signs and degrees to be placed on the Placidus System tenth to third house cusps; and we have seen that when we are setting up a chart by the Equal House System we only need to find the sign and degree on the Midheaven (Placidus tenth house cusp), and the sign, degree and minutes on the Ascendant. The other eleven house cusps derive from the Ascendant as will be shown presently when we calculate the cusps for Peter's chart.

But what of the *fourth to ninth* house cusps in the Placidus System? The signs on these cusps will be the *opposite* to those on the tenth to third cusps, the degrees being the same. As an example here are the twelve house cusps (Placidus) corresponding to sidereal time 0H.00M.00S. (Fig. 5).

10th cusp	is ♈ 0°	so 4th cusp is ♎ 0°
11th cusp	is ♉ 9°	so 5th cusp is ♏ 9°
12th cusp	is ♊ 22°	so 6th cusp is ♐ 22°
Asc. (1st) cusp is ♋ 26° 36′		so 7th cusp is ♑ 26° 36′
2nd cusp	is ♌ 12°	so 8th cusp is ♒ 12°
3rd cusp	is ♍ 3°	so 9th cusp is ♓ 3°

Intercepted Signs

One of the annoying features of Placidus charts is what is called *intercepted* signs. This is due to the considerable distortion that often occurs in the case of some of the houses, so that none of the thirty degrees of a sign "falls on" a cusp, but is intercepted between two cusps. This occurs in Peter's chart by Placidus and can be seen in Fig. 8.

Finding the Angles for Peter's Chart

We will now do a direct working with the local sidereal time at birth for our example case Peter, applying this to the *Tables of Houses* for the latitude of his birthplace.

On page 62 the *local sidereal time at Peter's birth* is given as 10H.47M.49S. Next we note that the latitude of his birthplace, Oxford, is 51° 45′ north.

The next step is to find the *nearest* latitude in the *Tables of Houses* to the latitude of birth, 51° 45′. In this case it is the latitude for London, 51° 32′ north, reproduced in Figs. 5 and 6.

We now refer to the sidereal time columns in Figs. 5 and 6, to find the *nearest* reading to the local sidereal time at Peter's birth (10H.47M.49S). The nearest reading is 10H.46M.09S. Can you find this?

As we are employing the Equal House System for Peter's chart we will first find the necessary angles corresponding to 10H.46M.09S. and then find what the house cusps for the Placidus System would be. The only two columns we need refer to for the Equal House System are:

Column two gives the Midheaven (M.C.)
Column five gives the Ascendant (1st house cusp).

The nearest sidereal time we are using is 10H.46M.09S. The corresponding figures in column two are *10*, and the sign at the top of the column is ♍ (Virgo). Thus, the approximate reading for the Midheaven for Peter's chart is ♍ 10°.

Now we look for the Ascendant. This is found in the *fifth* column corresponding to 10H.46M.09S. to be 20° 11'. Running our finger up the column until we come to a symbol for a zodiacal sign we find ♏ (Scorpio). The approximate Ascendant for Peter's chart is, therefore, ♏ 20° 11'.

The approximate *angles* for Peter's chart are found to be:

Ascendant: ♏ 20° 11'
Midheaven: ♍ 10° 00'

Finding the Placidus Cusps for Peter's Birth

The nearest sidereal time in the *Tables of Houses* to local sidereal time at Peter's birth we have found to be 10H.46M.09S. Now that each column in the tables has been explained to you this is how you should find the Placidus house cusps from Fig. 5:

10H.46M.09S. gives corresponding 10th cusp: ♍ 10°
10H.46M.09S. gives corresponding 11th cusp. ♎ 11°
10H.46M.09S. gives corresponding 12th cusp: ♏ 3°
10H.46M.09S. gives corresponding 1st cusp: ♏ 20° 11'
10H.46M.09S. gives corresponding 2nd cusp: ♐ 21°
10H.46M.09S. gives corresponding 3rd cusp: ♒ 0°
Opposite to 10th cusp sign gives 4th cusp: ♓ 10°
Opposite to 11th cusp sign gives 5th cusp: ♈ 11°
Opposite to 12th cusp sign gives 6th cusp: ♉ 3°
Opposite to 1st cusp sign gives 7th cusp: ♉ 20° 11'
Opposite to 2nd cusp sign gives 8th cusp: ♊ 21°
Opposite to 3rd cusp sign gives 9th cusp: ♌ 0°

♑ is intercepted in 2nd house
♋ is intercepted in 8th house

If you go carefully through the signs, beginning with ♈,
you will find that the symbol for Cancer (♋) is missing
between II and ♌. ♋ is therefore an intercepted sign. It
follows that the opposite sign to ♋ will also be intercepted, and we find that ♑ is intercepted in the 2nd house.
How to enter these signs on to the cusps for the Placidus
chart will be explained in Chapter 14.

Exercises

The answers to these exercises can be found in Appendix
VII.

66. Which factors in the birth-chart define the *angles?*

Referring to the *Tables of Houses* (Figs. 5 and 6), what
is the *nearest* sidereal time to the following local sidereal
times for births in London? What is the corresponding
Ascendant and Midheaven to the nearest sidereal time, in
each case?

67. 11H.15M.22S.
68. 21H.23M.42S.
69. 17H.59M.20S.
70. 12H.00M.00S.
71. 0H.01M.10S.
72. 23H.58M.58S.

Referring to Figs. 5 and 6, what signs and degrees are
on each of the 12 *Placidus* house cusps, corresponding to
these local sidereal times for births in London? Are there
any intercepted signs?

73. 5H.38M.12S.
74. 13H.13M.51S.
75. 0H.18M.21S.

10 *Calculating the Angles Exactly*

The beginner-student need not worry if he or she does not easily follow the formulae given in this chapter. It will be better understood and more quickly memorized if the student first has thoroughly grasped the method of finding the approximate angles as explained in Chapter 9.

I would suggest that the exact calculation of the angles is only applied when the given time is *accurately* known, or known within a ten minutes margin of error. The necessary calculations can be rather laborious, and therefore the angles would still be speculative if based on a given birth-time that has a margin of uncertainty. This would be the case even when the margin of uncertainty is only ten minutes (five minutes plus or minus given time), though an exact calculation of the angles to this given time would be worth doing.

As has been explained in the previous chapter, when we speak of calculating "the angles" we mean calculating "the Ascendant and the Midheaven (M.C.)."

There are *three* stages in the calculation of the exact angles:

Stage 1 Calculation of exact angles from *Tables of Houses* for nearest *lesser* latitude to latitude of birthplace (this latter is referred to in the formulae as the *given latitude*).

Stage 2 Calculation of exact angles from *Tables of Houses* for nearest *greater* latitude to latitude of birthplace.

Stage 3 Calculation of exact angles for *given* latitude (latitude of birthplace).

Calculation of Angles for Nearest Lesser Latitude

As an example calculation of exact angles we will use the local sidereal time for Peter's birth. As we already know, this reading is 10H.47M.49S.

If the student is to carefully follow each calculation step from the *Tables of Houses* it will be necessary to have the *Tables of Houses for Great Britain* (see Appendix III). It is anticipated that by the time the student is ready to learn exact calculation of the angles these tables will of necessity have been purchased as an essential reference book.

The latitude for Peter's birthplace, Oxford, was given as 51° 45′ north. The first thing we have to do is find the nearest *lesser* latitude to that of the birthplace. Opening the *Tables of Houses for Great Britain* we will find that the nearest latitude for which tables are given is the latitude for London, 51° 32′ north. This is convenient, since we have these reproduced in Figs. 5 and 6.

Do bear in mind that throughout this formulae the *given* sidereal time refers to the local sidereal time at birth.

We are now going to calculate the angles, using the *given* sidereal time (local sidereal time at Peter's birth). We know that this given sidereal time was arrived at by employing the *longitude* of Peter's birthplace. As yet we have had no cause to refer to the *latitude* of birthplace. For the first stage in calculation we have to assume that the *given sidereal time* refers to the *lesser* latitude, 51° 32′ north.

The given sidereal time is 10H.47M.49S. We have to find the nearest *earlier* sidereal time to that reading, and the nearest *later* sidereal time. We list these:

Given sidereal time	=	10H.47M.49S.
Nearest earlier sidereal time	=	10H.46M.09S.
Nearest later sidereal time	=	10H.49M.53S.

Calculation of M.C. (Nearest Lesser Latitude)

The formula is as follows:

$$\frac{B \times C}{A} = D \quad E = \text{M.C. at earlier sidereal time} + \text{D.}$$

A, B, C, D, and E are defined as follows:

A = the *difference*, expressed in seconds, between the nearest earlier sidereal time and the nearest later sidereal time.

B = the *difference*, expressed in seconds, between the nearest earlier sidereal time and the given sidereal time.

C = the *difference*, expressed in minutes of longitude, between the M.C. at earlier sidereal time and the M.C. at later sidereal time.

D = the *difference*, expressed in *minutes of longitude*, between the M.C. at earlier sidereal time and the M.C. at given sidereal time.

E = the *exact M.C.* at given sidereal time for nearest lesser latitude to latitude of birthplace.

To find A:

	H.	M.	S.
Nearest later sidereal time =	10	49	53
Nearest earlier sidereal time =	10	46	09
Difference =		3	44

$A = 3$ minutes 44 seconds, or 224 seconds.

To find B:

	H.	M.	S.
Given sidereal time =	10	47	49
Nearest earlier sidereal time =	10	46	09
Difference =		1	40

$B = 1$ minute 40 seconds, or 100 seconds.

To find C:

     M.C. at later sidereal time   =   ♍ 11°

M.C. at earlier sidereal time   =   ♍ 10°

Difference   = $\overline{1°}$

$C = 1$ degree, or 60 minutes.

To find D:

$$\frac{B \times C}{A} = D$$ Or, B multiplied by C, divided by A

Thus:

$$\frac{100 \times 60}{224} = \frac{6000}{224} \text{ or } 6000 \div 224$$

$$
\begin{array}{r}
26 \\
224\overline{)6000} \\
448 \\
\hline
1520 \\
1344 \\
\hline
176
\end{array}
$$

$D = 26$ minutes of longitude.

To find E:

M.C. at earlier sidereal time added to D.

Thus:

M.C. at earlier sidereal time   =   ♍ 10° 00′

D = $\overline{26′}$

E = ♍ 10° 26′

We have now found the exact M.C. at given sidereal time *for nearest lesser latitude* (51° 32′ north). It is ♍ 10° 26′.

Calculation of Ascendant (*Nearest Lesser Latitude*)

The formula is as follows:

$$\frac{B \times F}{A} = G$$ $H = $ Ascendant at earlier sidereal time $+ G$.

A and *B* have been defined on page 80. *F*, *G*, and *H* are defined as follows:

F = the *difference*, expressed in minutes of longitude, between the Ascendant at earlier sidereal time and the Ascendant at later sidereal time.

G = the *difference*, expressed in *minutes of longitude*, between the Ascendant at earlier sidereal time and the Ascendant at given sidereal time.

H = the *exact Ascendant* at given sidereal time for nearest lesser latitude to latitude of birthplace.

To find *F*:

Ascendant at later sidereal time   =   ♏ 20° 50'
Ascendant at earlier sidereal time   =   ♏ 20° 11'

Difference   =   39'

F = 39 minutes of longitude.

To find *G*:

$$\frac{B \times F}{A} = G \quad \text{Or, } B \text{ multiplied by } F \text{, divided by } A$$

Thus:

$$\frac{100 \times 39}{224} = \frac{3900}{224} \text{ or } 3900 \div 224$$

$$
\begin{array}{r}
17 \\
224)\overline{3900} \\
224 \\
\hline
1660 \\
1568 \\
\hline
92
\end{array}
$$

G = 17 minutes of longitude.

To find *H*:

Ascendant at earlier sidereal time added to *G*.

Thus:

Ascendant at earlier sidereal time = ♏ 20° 11'

$$G = \underline{\qquad 17'}$$

$$H = ♏\ 20°\ 28'$$

We have now found the exact Ascendant at given sidereal time *for nearest lesser latitude* (51° 32' north). It is ♏ 20° 28'.

Calculation of Ascendant (*Nearest Greater Latitude*)

We will now do the second stage in the calculation of exact angles for Peter's chart. We have to find the nearest *greater* latitude to the latitude of birthplace. Birthplace is Oxford, latitude 51° 45' north. In the *Tables of Houses for Great Britain* the next higher latitude given is that for Buckingham, 51° 59' north. The tables for this latitude will be used now.

There is no need to calculate the M.C. for the nearest *greater* latitude as this will be exactly the same as the M.C. for the *lesser* latitude that we have already calculated. If you scan through tables for different latitudes you will see that the corresponding M.C. to a given sidereal time will be identical.

In this second stage we only need to calculate the Ascendant for the nearest greater latitude.

The formula is as follows:

$$\frac{B \times I}{A} = J \quad K = \text{Ascendant at earlier sidereal time} + J$$

A and *B* have been defined on page 80. *I*, *J*, and *K* are defined as follows:

   I = the *difference*, expressed in minutes of longitude, between the Ascendant at earlier sidereal time and the Ascendant at later sidereal time.

   J = the *difference*, expressed in *minutes of longitude*

between the Ascendant at earlier sidereal time and the Ascendant at given sidereal time.

K = the *exact Ascendant* at given sidereal time for nearest greater latitude to latitude of birthplace.

To find I:

Ascendant at later sidereal time	=	♏ 20° 31′
Ascendant at earlier sidereal time	=	♏ 19° 52′
Difference	=	39′

I = 39 minutes of longitude.

To find J:

$$\frac{B \times I}{A} = J \quad \text{Or, } B \text{ multiplied by } I \text{, divided by } A$$

Thus:

$$\frac{100 \times 39}{224} = \frac{3900}{224} \quad \text{or } 3900 \div 224$$

$$\begin{array}{r} 17 \\ 224\overline{)3900} \\ 224 \\ \hline 1660 \\ 1568 \\ \hline 92 \end{array}$$

J = 17 minutes of longitude.

It will be noticed that J in our example case is identical to the similar calculation for G. This is not always so.

To find K:

Ascendant at earlier sidereal time added to J.

Thus:

Ascendant at earlier sidereal time	=	♏ 19° 52′
J	=	17′
K	=	♏ 20° 09′

We have now found the exact Ascendant at given sidereal time *for nearest greater latitude* (51° 59′ north). It is ♏ 20° 09′.

Calculation of Ascendant for Given Latitude

We are now on *Stage 3* in the calculation of exact angles for Peter's chart. We have already seen that there was only the need to calculate the exact position of the M.C. once, which we did for the nearest lesser latitude. Providing we used the same sidereal times we could have used the *Tables of Houses* for any latitude, and arrived at the same longitude position for the M.C. We therefore know what the exact M.C. is for the given latitude, that is, for Peter's birthplace. It is the result of calculation step *E* that we did: ♍ 10° 26′.

All that we need to know now is, what is the *exact Ascendant for the given latitude*?

The formula is as follows:

$$\frac{M \times N}{L} = O$$

P (Ascendant at given latitude) =

$H + O$ if given sidereal time falls between 18H.00M.00S. and 5H.59M.59S.
or $H - O$ if given sidereal time falls between 6H.00M.00S. and 17H.59M.59S.

H has been defined on page 82. *L*, *M*, *N*, *O*, and *P* are defined as follows:

L = the *difference*, expressed in minutes of latitude, between the nearest lesser latitude and the nearest greater latitude.

M = the *difference*, expressed in minutes of latitude, between the given latitude and the nearest lesser latitude.

N = the *difference*, expressed in minutes of longitude, between the Ascendant at nearest lesser latitude (H) and the Ascendant at nearest greater latitude (K).

O = the *difference*, expressed in minutes of longitude, between the Ascendant at nearest lesser latitude (H) and the Ascendant at given latitude.

P = the *exact Ascendant* at given sidereal time for the given latitude (latitude of birthplace).

To find L:

The nearest lesser latitude is subtracted from the nearest greater latitude.

Nearest greater latitude	=	51° 59′
Nearest lesser latitude	=	51° 32′
Difference	=	27′

L=27 minutes of latitude.

To find M:

The nearest lesser latitude is subtracted from the given latitude.

Given latitude	=	51° 45′
Nearest lesser latitude	=	51° 32′
Difference	=	13′

M=13 minutes of latitude.

To find N:

The Ascendant at nearest lesser latitude (H) is subtracted from the Ascendant at nearest greater latitude (K) if given sidereal time *falls between 18H.00M.00S. and 5H.59M.59S.*

or

the Ascendant at nearest greater latitude (K) is subtracted from the Ascendant at nearest lesser latitude (H) if given sidereal time *falls between 6H.00M.00S and 17H.59M.59S.*

In our example case the given sidereal time is 10H.47M.49S., therefore the Ascendant at nearest greater latitude (*K*) is subtracted from the Ascendant at nearest lesser latitude (*H*).

Ascendant at nearest lesser latitude (*H*) = ♏ 20° 28′
Ascendant at nearest greater latitude (*K*) = ♏ 20° 09′

Difference = 19′

N = 19 minutes of longitude.

To find *O*:

$$\frac{M \times N}{L} = O \quad \text{Or, } M \text{ multiplied by } N, \text{ divided by } L$$

Thus:

$$\frac{13 \times 19}{27} = 247 \div 27$$

$$27\overline{)247} \atop 9$$

$$243$$

$$4$$

O = 9 minutes of longitude.

To find *P*:

We need to be careful at this point as to whether *H* is added to *O*, or *O* is subtracted from *H*, as indicated on page 85.

The given sidereal time is 10H.47M.49S. (that is, the local sidereal time at Peter's birth). This reading falls between 6H.00M.00S. and 17H.59M.59S., therefore:

formula is *H* minus *O*

(*H*) Ascendant at nearest lesser latitude = ♏ 20° 28′
(*O*) = 9′

(*P*) Ascendant at given latitude = ♏ 20° 19′

We have now calculated the *exact* angles for Peter's

birth-chart. In the next chapter we will learn how to enter these on to the chart:

Peter's Ascendant   =   ♏ 20° 19'
Peter's Midheaven (M.C.)   =   ♍ 10° 26'

In the above calculations of N and P there is need to be very careful to note whether there is an *increase* or *decrease* in the Ascendant's longitude between different latitudes. Perhaps a word or two of extra explanation should be given. If you possess either of the two booklets of *Tables of Houses* recommended in Appendix III, you can easily note for yourself the following:

(*a*) As latitude increases, the Ascendant at corresponding sidereal times will *increase*, when sidereal time falls between 18H.00M.00S. and 5H.59M.59S.

(*b*) As latitude increases, the Ascendant at corresponding sidereal times will *decrease*, when sidereal time falls between 6H.00M.00S. and 17H.59M.59S.

Here is an example for (*a*) above by reference to *Raphael's Tables of Houses for Northern Latitudes*, using the same sidereal time figures for several consecutive latitudes:

| | Sidereal | |
Latitude	Time	Ascendant
22° 33' N.	3H.51M.15S. corresponds to	♍ 0° 30'
23° 12' N.	3H.51M.15S. corresponds to	♍ 0° 39'
24° 27' N.	3H.51M.15S. corresponds to	♍ 0° 55'
25° 19' N.	3H.51M.15S. corresponds to	♍ 1° 06'

Sidereal time shown above is the same for the four different latitudes, but because this sidereal time is between 18H.00M.00S. and 5H.59M.59S. the Ascendant is seen to increase with increase in latitude.

Here is an example for (*b*) above by reference to the same booklet of tables and using the same latitudes employed in the example for (*a*), but with another sidereal time reading:

Latitude	Sidereal Time		Ascendant
22° 33' N.	15H.51M.15S.	corresponds to	♒ 18° 56'
23° 12' N.	15H.51M.15S.	corresponds to	♒ 18° 40'
24° 27' N.	15H.51M.15S.	corresponds to	♒ 18° 11'
25° 19' N.	15H.51M.15S.	corresponds to	♒ 17° 50'

We now see that because the given sidereal time is between 6H.00M.00S. and 17H.59M.59S. with increase in latitude the Ascendant *decreases* in longitude.

Actually, the Ascendant corresponding to sidereal time 6H.00M.00S., and the Ascendant corresponding to sidereal time 18H.00M.00S., are exactly the same for *all* latitudes respectively. The corresponding Ascendant to sidereal time 6H.00M.00S. is ♎ 0° 00'; and the corresponding Ascendant to sidereal time 18H.00M.00S. is ♈ 0° 00'. This applies to equivalent latitudes north or south of the equator.

Exercise

The answers to each part of this exercise can be found in Appendix VII. For this exercise you will need to refer to *Raphael's Tables of Houses for Great Britain*.

76. A birth occurs in latitude 57° 49' north. The local sidereal time at birth is 17H.34M.28S. Calculate the exact Ascendant and Midheaven, and give the answers to each step, A, B, C, D, E, F, G, H, I, J, K, L, M, N, O, and P, respectively.

11 *Entering Angles and Signs in the Chart*

In Chapter 10 we calculated the *exact* angles for Peter's chart. These differed slightly from the approximate positions we arrived at in Chapter 9. We will, of course, use the exact angles:

        Peter's Ascendant: ♏ 20° 19′
        Peter's Midheaven (M.C.):   ♍ 10° 26′

If you turn to Fig. 1 you will see the basic framework of the natal chart before the signs and planets have been

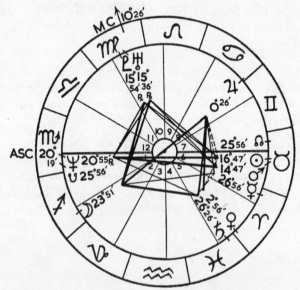

Fig. 7. Peter's chart by Equal House System.

entered. You will see the difference if you refer to Fig. 7
which is the completed chart for Peter, showing the signs
against the house cusps and the planets placed next to the
signs they are in.

The Ascendant and Decendant

In Fig. 1 the angles are shown in their relationship to the
twelve houses of the chart. The Ascendant is always at
the *eastern* point of the horizon. Its opposite point in the
ecliptic, the Descendant, is always at the *western* point of
the horizon. The smallest circle in the centre of the chart
symbolizes the Earth, or the man standing on Earth. This
is the very core of the chart. If he stands facing south, with
his arms outstretched horizontally, his left hand will point
directly to the eastern horizon of his locality, and his right
hand will point directly to the western horizon.

The M.C. and I.C.

The name the astrologer gives to the *upper meridian*
(where the ecliptic intersects the meridian circle of birthplace) is the *Midheaven*, which we have seen is usually
abbreviated to *M.C.* Its name conveys its essential associa-
tion with the birthplace: *mid*-heaven.

The opposite point in the ecliptic to the Midheaven is the
lower meridian or *I.C.* These two points are joined by an
imaginary line that is known as an *angle* of the astrological
chart. We never draw this line right through the chart.
In Fig. 1 both points are shown by arrows crossing the
outer circles of the chart, and as an illustration of the
angle they represent these arrows are joined with a dotted
line.

The Houses in the Natal Chart

There are twelve *mundane houses* in the chart, forming a symmetrical pattern within the basic framework.

Traditionally these are called *mundane* houses, because they are twelve symbolic divisions of the life of man concerned with mundane affairs, earthly matters. Nowadays we simply call these *houses*, omitting the "mundane".

In Fig. 1 the twelve houses are shown in their *fixed* positions. Whereas the planets and the signs can be "progressed" to move relative to the years of a person's life in an anticlockwise direction (clockwise direction when a planet is retrograde), the houses have their permanent positions in the chart.

The *first* house is always beneath the eastern horizon, and its cusp is the degree and sign rising at the *Ascendant*.

The *cusp* is the point of division between two houses. It is also the *beginning* of the house it is connected with. The thirty degrees in a house (Equal House System) begin at its cusp and are counted in an anticlockwise direction, following the true or direct motion of the planets and signs, in the same way that the thirty degrees in a sign are counted. A fault with many beginners is to enter planets incorrectly, by placing them on the wrong side of a house cusp, because instead of counting the degrees in an anticlockwise direction they do this in a clockwise direction.

The student will notice that as the 1st house is always at the Ascendant, so is the opposite house, the 7th, always at the Descendant. But don't be misled by Fig. 1 in thinking that the M.C. is always placed in the 9th house as shown. According to the latitude of birthplace and the time and season of birth the M.C. may normally be placed anywhere between the 8th and 11th houses. The nearer we get to the polar latitudes so is there the likelihood of the M.C. being found closer to the horizon, in the 7th or 12th houses.

Entering Angles and Signs in Equal House Chart

We will enter the angles and the signs on to the basic framework of Peter's chart. I want you to do this as an exercise. If you have not yet bought a supply of printed chart-forms you can make your own chart by copying the framework drawn in Fig. 1. But don't enter the M.C. and I.C. as shown in Fig. 1. Simply draw the two outer circles of the "wheel" and enter the twelve "spokes" or house cusps, using a protractor if possible so that you make each house of equal thirty degrees size.

The first thing to do is *enter the Ascendant on the 1st house cusp*. Peter's Ascendant is ♏ 20° 19′. Write the degrees and minutes first, directly in line with the 1st cusp. Write your figures boldly so that they are clear to read. You can see how "20° 19′" have been entered in Fig. 7. Before we enter the symbol for Scorpio we must put in the dividing lines between the signs. Each sign is thirty degrees in length. The Ascendant in Peter's case is 20°, therefore two-thirds or twenty degrees of the Rising Sign will be *above* the horizon, and only one-third or ten degrees beneath the horizon. This means that the line dividing Scorpio (♏) and Sagittarius (♐) will be drawn in about one-third of the distance into the 1st house. Likewise, the line dividing Sagittarius and Capricorn (♑) will be drawn in one-third of the distance into the 2nd house, and so on, because signs and houses are of equal thirty degrees length. I want you to do this now, and compare what you have done with the sign-divisions in Fig. 7.

Having entered 20° 19′ on Peter's chart's Ascendant, and drawn in the twelve sign-divisions, we enter the symbol ♏ just above 20° 19′ at the Ascendant. Note how it is done in Fig. 7. As the houses are of equal length there is no need to write 20° 19′ against each cusp. We will know this is the same for each cusp, as it is at the Ascendant. But each sign must be entered neatly midway between the sign-divisions as shown in Fig. 7. Although, as has been said, there is no need to enter "20° 19′" against every house cusp, these will be the readings for each of the twelve cusps in Peter's Equal House chart:

1st house cusp	=	♏	20° 19′
2nd house cusp	=	♐	20° 19′
3rd house cusp	=	♑	20° 19′
4th house cusp	=	♒	20° 19′
5th house cusp	=	♓	20° 19′
6th house cusp	=	♈	20° 19′
7th house cusp	=	♉	20° 19′
8th house cusp	=	♊	20° 19′
9th house cusp	=	♋	20° 19′
10th house cusp	=	♌	20° 19′
11th house cusp	=	♍	20° 19′
12th house cusp	=	♎	20° 19′

Finally the M.C. has to be entered. For Peter's chart this is ♍ 10° 26′. 10° is one-third of 30°, and so we draw a neat small arrow (as shown in Fig. 7) about one-third through the thirty degrees section that represents the sign of ♍. To make the arrow distinct, it should project beyond the outside circle of the chart, so at a glance we can see that the M.C. "falls in" the 10th house and in Virgo. The astrologer does not usually bother to enter the I.C. He knows it will be the opposite point to the M.C., but you may if you wish enter it, at ♓ 10° 26′ in the 4th house.

Every chart I set up I always write the Ascending sign and the sign in which the M.C. falls, in *red* ink. The other ten signs I enter in blue or black, whichever I'm using. By doing this the two important factors in the chart, Ascendant and M.C., are clearly distinguished from the rest of the signs.

Entering Signs in Placidus System Chart

Peter's chart in terms of the Placidus House System is shown in Fig. 8. Note that with this system no sign-divisions are drawn in. The sign and degree corresponding to a house cusp is written against that cusp. An *intercepted* sign is entered midway through the house it is intercepted in, as shown in Fig. 8 for ♋ and ♑. ♋ is intercepted in the 8th house, and ♑ is intercepted in the 2nd house. On page 76 we listed the readings for each house cusp for Peter's chart, so get out a fresh chart-form and see if you can enter the signs and degrees as illustrated in Fig. 8. Note that in Fig. 8 the *exact* angles are used, and not the approximate angles listed on page 76.

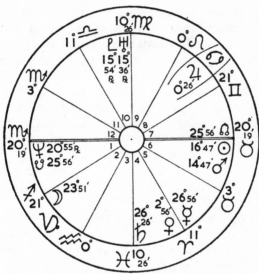

Fig. 8. Peter's chart by Placidus House System.

12 *How to Use Proportional Logarithms*

Logarithms are labour-saving methods of calculation. Various tables of logarithms are in use, which are certain numbers calculated by mathematicians, but the astrologer has cause only to refer to the tables of *proportional logarithms*. These tables are always given at the back of *Raphael's Ephemerides*, and they are reproduced in Fig. 9.

I have quite frequently had new students write to me saying they are completely awed by these tables, and they feel sure they will never be able to use them. I am sure that any student who obtains this book will never have cause to look upon logarithms (we will call them *logs.* for short) as complicated, but will welcome them for what they are: simple-to-use labour-savers.

It is not necessary to explain here the principles underlying logs. and their uses. It will suffice to say that logarithmic tables can save one lengthy and laborious operations of multiplication, division, involution and evolution, as well as there being some calculations which would be practically impossible without logs.

By means of logs., *the processes of multiplication and division are converted into the more simpler processes of addition and subtraction.* Thus, to multiply numbers together, their logs. are *added*, and to divide them their logs. are *subtracted*.

I am devoting this chapter to the explanation of proportional logarithms so that we can go ahead and use these in the calculation of the planets' positions at our example case Peter's birth in the next chapter, without having to

PROPORTIONAL LOGARITHMS FOR FINDING THE PLANETS' PLACES

Min.	0	1	2	3	4	5	6	7	8	9	10	11	12	13	14	15	Min.
0	3.1584	1.3802	1.0792	9031	7781	6812	6021	5351	4771	4260	3802	3388	3010	2663	2341	2041	0
1	3.1584	1.3730	1.0756	9007	7763	6798	6009	5341	4762	4252	3795	3382	3004	2657	2336	2036	1
2	2.8573	1.3660	1.0720	8983	7745	6784	5997	5330	4753	4244	3788	3375	2998	2652	2330	2032	2
3	2.6812	1.3590	1.0685	8959	7728	6769	5985	5320	4744	4236	3780	3368	2992	2646	2325	2027	3
4	2.5563	1.3522	1.0649	8935	7710	6755	5973	5310	4735	4228	3773	3362	2986	2640	2320	2022	4
5	2.4594	1.3454	1.0614	8912	7692	6741	5961	5300	4726	4220	3766	3355	2980	2635	2315	2017	5
6	2.3802	1.3388	1.0580	8888	7674	6726	5949	5289	4717	4212	3759	3349	2974	2629	2310	2012	6
7	2.3133	1.3323	1.0546	8865	7657	6712	5937	5279	4708	4204	3752	3342	2968	2624	2305	2008	7
8	2.2553	1.3258	1.0511	8842	7639	6698	5925	5269	4699	4196	3745	3336	2962	2618	2300	2003	8
9	2.2041	1.3195	1.0478	8819	7622	6684	5913	5259	4690	4188	3737	3329	2956	2613	2295	1998	9
10	2.1584	1.3133	1.0444	8796	7604	6670	5902	5249	4682	4180	3730	3323	2950	2607	2289	1993	10
11	2.1170	1.3071	1.0411	8773	7587	6656	5890	5239	4673	4172	3723	3316	2944	2602	2284	1988	11
12	2.0792	1.3010	1.0378	8751	7570	6642	5878	5229	4664	4164	3716	3310	2938	2596	2279	1984	12
13	2.0444	1.2950	1.0345	8728	7552	6628	5866	5219	4655	4156	3709	3303	2933	2591	2274	1979	13
14	2.0122	1.2891	1.0313	8706	7535	6614	5855	5209	4646	4148	3702	3297	2927	2585	2269	1974	14
15	1.9823	1.2833	1.0280	8683	7518	6600	5843	5199	4638	4141	3695	3291	2921	2580	2264	1969	15
16	1.9542	1.2775	1.0248	8661	7501	6587	5832	5189	4629	4133	3688	3284	2915	2574	2259	1965	16
17	1.9279	1.2719	1.0216	8639	7484	6573	5820	5179	4620	4125	3681	3278	2909	2569	2254	1960	17
18	1.9031	1.2663	1.0185	8617	7467	6559	5809	5169	4611	4117	3674	3271	2903	2564	2249	1955	18
19	1.8796	1.2607	1.0153	8595	7451	6546	5797	5159	4603	4109	3667	3265	2897	2558	2244	1950	19
20	1.8573	1.2553	1.0122	8573	7434	6532	5786	5149	4594	4102	3660	3258	2891	2553	2239	1946	20
21	1.8361	1.2499	1.0091	8552	7417	6519	5774	5139	4585	4094	3653	3252	2885	2547	2234	1941	21
22	1.8159	1.2445	1.0061	8530	7401	6505	5763	5129	4577	4086	3646	3246	2880	2542	2229	1936	22
23	1.7966	1.2393	1.0030	8509	7384	6492	5752	5120	4568	4079	3639	3239	2874	2536	2223	1932	23
24	1.7781	1.2341	1.0000	8487	7368	6478	5740	5110	4559	4071	3632	3233	2868	2531	2218	1927	24
25	1.7604	1.2289	0.9970	8466	7351	6465	5729	5100	4551	4063	3625	3227	2862	2525	2213	1922	25
26	1.7434	1.2239	0.9940	8445	7335	6451	5718	5090	4542	4055	3618	3220	2856	2520	2208	1917	26
27	1.7270	1.2188	0.9910	8424	7318	6438	5706	5081	4534	4048	3611	3214	2850	2515	2203	1913	27
28	1.7112	1.2139	0.9881	8403	7302	6425	5695	5071	4525	4040	3604	3208	2845	2509	2198	1908	28
29	1.6960	1.2090	0.9852	8382	7286	6412	5684	5061	4516	4032	3597	3201	2839	2504	2193	1903	29
30	1.6812	1.2041	0.9823	8361	7270	6398	5673	5051	4508	4025	3590	3195	2833	2499	2188	1899	30
31	1.6670	1.1993	0.9794	8341	7254	6385	5662	5042	4499	4017	3583	3189	2827	2493	2183	1894	31
32	1.6532	1.1946	0.9765	8320	7238	6372	5651	5032	4491	4010	3576	3183	2821	2488	2178	1889	32
33	1.6398	1.1899	0.9737	8300	7222	6359	5640	5023	4482	4002	3570	3176	2816	2483	2173	1885	33
34	1.6269	1.1852	0.9708	8279	7206	6346	5629	5013	4474	3994	3563	3170	2810	2477	2168	1880	34
35	1.6143	1.1806	0.9680	8259	7190	6333	5618	5003	4466	3987	3556	3164	2804	2472	2164	1875	35
36	1.6021	1.1761	0.9652	8239	7174	6320	5607	4994	4457	3979	3549	3157	2798	2467	2159	1871	36
37	1.5902	1.1716	0.9625	8219	7159	6307	5596	4984	4449	3972	3542	3151	2793	2461	2154	1866	37
38	1.5786	1.1671	0.9597	8199	7143	6294	5585	4975	4440	3964	3535	3145	2787	2456	2149	1862	38
39	1.5673	1.1627	0.9570	8179	7128	6282	5574	4965	4432	3957	3529	3139	2781	2451	2144	1857	39
40	1.5563	1.1584	0.9542	8159	7112	6269	5563	4956	4424	3949	3522	3133	2775	2445	2139	1852	40
41	1.5456	1.1540	0.9515	8140	7097	6256	5552	4947	4415	3942	3515	3126	2770	2440	2134	1848	41
42	1.5351	1.1498	0.9488	8120	7081	6243	5541	4937	4407	3934	3508	3120	2764	2435	2129	1843	42
43	1.5249	1.1455	0.9462	8101	7066	6231	5531	4928	4399	3927	3501	3114	2758	2430	2124	1838	43
44	1.5149	1.1413	0.9435	8081	7050	6218	5520	4918	4390	3919	3495	3108	2753	2424	2119	1834	44
45	1.5051	1.1372	0.9409	8062	7035	6205	5509	4909	4382	3912	3488	3102	2747	2419	2114	1829	45
46	1.4956	1.1331	0.9383	8043	7020	6193	5498	4900	4374	3905	3481	3096	2741	2414	2109	1825	46
47	1.4863	1.1290	0.9356	8023	7005	6180	5488	4890	4365	3897	3475	3089	2736	2409	2104	1820	47
48	1.4771	1.1249	0.9330	8004	6990	6168	5477	4881	4357	3890	3468	3083	2730	2403	2099	1816	48
49	1.4682	1.1209	0.9305	7985	6975	6155	5466	4872	4349	3882	3461	3077	2724	2398	2095	1811	49
50	1.4594	1.1170	0.9279	7966	6960	6143	5456	4863	4341	3875	3454	3071	2719	2393	2090	1806	50
51	1.4508	1.1130	0.9254	7947	6945	6131	5445	4853	4333	3868	3448	3065	2713	2388	2085	1802	51
52	1.4424	1.1091	0.9228	7929	6930	6118	5435	4844	4324	3860	3441	3059	2707	2382	2080	1797	52
53	1.4341	1.1053	0.9203	7910	6915	6106	5424	4835	4316	3853	3434	3053	2702	2377	2075	1793	53
54	1.4260	1.1015	0.9178	7891	6900	6094	5414	4826	4308	3846	3427	3047	2696	2372	2070	1788	54
55	1.4180	1.0977	0.9153	7873	6885	6081	5403	4817	4300	3838	3421	3041	2691	2367	2065	1784	55
56	1.4102	1.0939	0.9128	7854	6871	6069	5393	4808	4292	3831	3415	3034	2685	2362	2061	1779	56
57	1.4025	1.0902	0.9104	7836	6856	6057	5382	.4798	4284	3824	3408	3028	2679	2356	2056	1774	57
58	1.3949	1.0865	0.9079	7818	6841	6045	5372	4789	4276	3817	3401	3022	2674	2351	2051	1770	58
59	1.3875	1.0828	0.9055	7800	6827	6033	5361	4780	4268	3809	3395	3016	2668	2346	2046	1765	59
	0	1	2	3	4	5	6	7	8	9	10	11	12	13	14	15	

RULE:—Add proportional log. of planet's daily motion to log. of time from noon, and the sum will be the log. of the motion required. Add this to planet's place at noon, if time be p.m., but subtract if a.m. and the sum will be planet's true place. If Retrograde, subtract for p.m., but add for a.m.

What is the Long. of ☽ April 29th, 1966 at 2.15 p.m.? ☽'s daily motion—14° 26′

Prop. Log. of 14° 26′	...	...	.2208
Prop. Log. of 2h. 15m.	...	...	1.0280
☽'s motion in 2h. 15m. = 1° 21′ or Log.			1.2488

☽'s Long. on April 29th = 26° ♌ 30′ + 1° 21′ = 27° ♌ 51′.
The Daily Motions of the Sun, Moon, Mars, Venus and Mercury will be found on pages 26 to 28.

Fig. 9

perhaps confuse matters with explaining the use of logs. then.

The only use the astrologer has for these tables of logs. is to enable him to quickly and accurately calculate *proportional values*. For instance, this is a typical calculation that could have to be made, when finding the exact position in longitude of the Moon at a given birth:

Birth-time is given as 7.21 p.m. G.M.T., 25th May 1966.
The Moon's position at noon G.M.T. 25th May is ♌ 9° 03'.

The Moon's position at noon G.M.T. on the *following* day, 26th May, is ♌ 23° 15'. Moon's motion, therefore, in the 24 hours between consecutive noon positions is 14° 12'.

The question is:

If the Moon travels 14° 12' in this given period of 24 hours, how far does the Moon travel in 7 hours 21 minutes, which is the interval from noon to the given time of birth?

In other words, we are wanting to know:

If 24 hours correspond to 14° 12', what *proportion* of 24 hours is 7 hours 21 minutes, to enable us to find the *corresponding proportion of 14° 12'* ?

The average student would be forgiven if he or she was at a loss to know how to calculate this proportion, and the practising astrologer would be forgiven if he assessed this proportion approximately to avoid spending valuable time on such a laborious calculation. It is only for calculating the exact position of each planet that this proportion of a planet's 24-hour's motion is required. Yet when it is seen that this calculation would need to be made for the Sun, the Moon, Mercury, Venus and Mars for most charts, one realizes what a lot of time would be spent on this portion of chart calculation.

But with the *Tables of Proportional Logarithms* to refer

to one can quickly calculate each planet's position. Presently we will do the above example together with the use of the logs., but first the tables given in Fig. 9 need to be explained.

The tables are comprised of eighteen *vertical columns* of figures. The heading at the top of these columns states *Degrees or Hours*. This means the figures *from 0 to 15* heading each of the sixteen middle columns can be thought of as either *degrees of longitude*, or *hours of mean time*. For convenience, these same figures from 0 to 15 are repeated at the foot of each respective column.

The *first* and the *last* of the vertical columns are headed *Min*. This is an abbreviation for *minutes*. The minutes, reading down the column, are from *0 to 59*. The minutes can be thought of as either minutes *of longitude*, or minutes *of mean time*. This will be better understood with an example.

What is the logarithm oj 2 hours 12 minutes of mean time?

Moving our finger horizontally along the figures given at the top of each column we stop when we come to *2*. This is the *2 hours* we have to find. Keeping our finger on that column, but our eyes on the *first* column in which are listed *minutes*, we slowly run our finger down the column headed *2* until we come to the figures *in line with 12 minutes*. The figures given at the point of intersection of the 2 hours vertical column and and the 12 minutes horizontal line will be the logarithm for 2 hours 12 minutes. These figures are: 1·0378.

Here is another example, this time using degrees and minutes of longitude. *What is the logarithm of 13 degrees 54 minutes of longitude?*

As with the previous example, we run our finger along the figures given at the top of each column until we come to *13*, which represents 13°. Keeping our finger on that column we now look at the *last* column in which *minutes* are given (in this case we refer to this last column because it is nearer to the 13° column than is the first column of minutes). We slowly move our finger down the 13° column until we come to the line of figures corresponding to the required *54 minutes*. At this point of intersection of the 13° column and the line horizontal with 54′ we can read: *2372*. Although the decimal point is not shown, the actual reading is ·*2372*. If you look at the figures listed in columns two, three, and four, you will see that the decimal point is shown. It is not shown in the other columns for convenience, to save space. However, we have in our example above found the logarithm for 13° 54′ of longitude. It is ·2372, or, if you prefer, 0·2372.

Finding the Moon's Position by Logs.

Near the beginning of this chapter I gave an example of a typical calculation that could have to be made, when finding the exact position in longitude of the Moon at a given time of birth. We will now do this calculation with the use of logs. and with the data that was given.

Birth-time is given as 7.21 p.m. G.M.T., 25th May 1966. As birth is *after* noon (p.m.) the *interval* from noon to birth is *7 hours 21 minutes*. This we know as the *interval value*.

Our next step is to find the *daily motion* of the Moon, or the distance in terms of longitude the Moon has travelled from the noon *prior to* birth-time until the *following* noon. In other words, this will be the distance travelled by the Moon in a given period of 24 hours between consecutive noon positions. *Raphael's Ephemeris* for any year usually gives on pages 26–28 the complete daily motions of the Sun, Moon, Mercury, Venus and Mars in terms of longitude for each day of the year, and also the daily motion of the Moon in terms of declination.

These are most useful, since they save us the trouble of working out these motions by extracting the difference between a planet's two consecutive noon positions. Fig. 10 shows a reproduction of a portion of page 27 from *Raphael's 1966 Ephemeris*, covering the daily motions of the planets for May.

The first column headed *D* gives the thirty-one days of the month. Moon's longitude is given in the *third* column, as indicated by the Moon's symbol (☽) at the head of the column. The figures shown are in degrees, minutes and seconds. The daily motion is for the 24 hours from noon on the corresponding date. For example, the Moon's daily motion, or the distance it travels in 24 hours from noon on the 1st May to noon on the 2nd May, is 14° 31′ 10″.

We will now find the Moon's daily motion from noon on the 25th May 1966 for the example we are doing. Referring to Fig. 10 we find that the Moon's motion given against the 25th May is 14° 11′ 54″. We "round this off" to 14° 12′. This is because of the following rule the student should note:

(a) Seconds of longitude are too insignificant to be bothered with in calculations. Therefore,

(b) When seconds are *less than 30″*, these should be ignored;

(c) When seconds are *30″ or over* convert these into one whole minute of longitude and add to minutes given.

As a point of interest, we will check this daily motion of the Moon (14° 12′) with the result we shall obtain by a method that takes just a little longer than by reference to the page of the ephemeris reproduced in Fig. 10. We will refer to Fig. 3. This shows a reproduction of one of the two pages for May 1966 appearing in *Raphael's Ephemeris* for that year. It is the left-hand page for that month. Here we can find the position of the Moon for noon on each day of May 1966. Most readers will probably have my book, *How to Read the Ephemeris*, and will be conversant with the various columns of figures shown in Fig. 3. Column six in the lower portion of the page is headed " ☽ Long.", indicating that in this column are the positions for the Moon in terms of longitude for noon of each day. We are interested in the Moon's position on the 25th and its position on the 26th. You will find they are as follows:

Moon's position at noon 26th May   =   ♌ 23° 15'
Moon's position at noon 25th May   =   ♌ 9° 03'

Difference, or daily motion   =   14° 12'

You will see that I have ignored the seconds of longitude, because the figures given are *less than 30"*. Naturally the Moon's position on the later date, the 26th, will be greater than its position on the 25th. Therefore as we want to subtract the lesser position from the greater position to find what is the Moon's daily motion between noon 25th and noon 26th, the position of the Moon on the 26th has been written first, and beneath it the position on the 25th. The difference, or daily motion, is 14° 12'. Which is, of course, exactly what we found the motion to be by our quicker method of referring to the already computed daily motions shown in Fig. 10.

We can now work with the table of logarithms and find the Moon's position at 7.21 p.m. G.M.T. on the 25th May 1966 for our example calculation. We have found the two necessary factors:

Interval from noon to birth = 7 hours 21 minutes
Moon's daily motion   = 14° 12'

We proceed as follows:

1. Find the log. of interval value.
2. Find the log. of Moon's daily motion.

3. Add the log. of interval value to the log. of Moon's daily motion. The result is the log. of the addition.
4. Find the *antilogarithm* of the log. of the addition. The antilogarithm will give us the distance or motion travelled by the Moon during the interval from noon to birth.

Step 1. Find the log. of interval value. The interval value is 7 hours 21 minutes. Remembering how you were shown to use the table of logs. earlier in this chapter we first run our finger along the "hours" figures at the top of the columns (Fig. 9) until we stop at *7 hours*. Next we move our finger down this column until we come level with *21 minutes* (21 in the minutes column). The intersection of the vertical and the horizontal lines of figures pin-point for us the log. of the interval value. It is *·5139*.

Step 2. Find the log. of Moon's daily motion. The Moon's daily motion we have found to be 14° 12'. The figures in the table of logs. that we have used for *hours* now become *degrees*. Running our finger along these figures we stop at *14*. Next we move our finger down this column until we are level with the line of figures corresponding to *12* in the column of minutes. We find the log. of the Moon's daily motion, and it is *·2279*.

Step 3. We have to *add* the log. of the interval value to the log. of the Moon's daily motion. This we do:

Log. of interval value	=	·5139
Log. of Moon's daily motion	=	·2279
Log. of addition	=	·7418

Step 4. Find the *antilog.* of the log. of addition. What *is* meant by the *antilog.* or *antilogarithm*? The purpose of logarithmic calculations is to *find a number*. In our example case the number we are looking for will correspond to the Moon's motion during the interval from noon to birth-

time. The key to finding this number by proportional logarithms is the log. of the addition. This we calculated in *Step 3*. It is ·*7418*. What we must now do is *find the antilogarithm of* ·*7418*. The antilogarithm will be the number corresponding to the Moon's motion during the interval from noon to birth-time.

The operation is exactly opposite to that of finding a log. We have to refer to the table of logs. and find the number *nearest to* the log. of addition. This number will be at the point of intersection of the *column of degrees* and the *line corresponding to the minutes* of the antilog.

The log. of addition in our example is ·*7418*. Referring to the table of logs. we look for a number *nearest to* ·*7418*. This will be found in the *sixth* column. The nearest number is ·*7417*. Running our finger carefully up this column we note that this column corresponds to 4 degrees. Remember that the antilog. we are looking for will be in terms of *longitude* and not time, therefore the *4* at the top of the sixth column refers to *degrees* and not to hours. Still keeping our finger-tip against the "key number" ·7417 we must now note how many *minutes* of longitude this number corresponds to. It is *21 minutes*.

We have found the antilog. of the log. of addition to correspond to 4° 21′ of longitude. This is the distance travelled by the Moon during the interval from noon on the 25th May 1966 to the given birth-time, 7.21 p.m. G.M.T. In other words, the Moon's motion in 7 hours 21 minutes was 4° 21′.

All that we have to do now to find what is the position of the Moon *at 7.21 p.m. G.M.T.* is to *add* this interval motion to the Moon's position at noon on the 25th May. This interval motion has to be *added* to the noon position because birth occurred in the second half of the day, that is, *after* noon. By reference to Fig. 3 we have already found that the Moon's position at noon on the 25th May 1966 was ♌ 9° 03′. To this we add the interval motion:

Moon's position at noon 25th May   =   ♌ 9° 03'
Moon's interval motion, noon to birth =   4° 21'
———————————
Moon's position at 7.21 p.m. G.M.T.   =   ♌ 13° 24'

Exercises

The answers to these exercises will be found in Appendix VII.

What is the logarithm of each of the following:

77. 3 hours 24 minutes of mean time.
78. 11 hours 00 minutes of mean time.
79. 0 hours 59 minutes of mean time.
80. 4 degrees 28 minutes of longitude.
81. 15 degrees 12 minutes of longitude.
82. 8 degrees 30 minutes of longitude.

What is the antilogarithm of each of the following logs. of addition, in terms of longitude:

83. 2·3133.
84. 0·3149.
85. 0·9899.
86. 1·1868.

Using the following interval values and daily motions of the Moon, find (*a*) the log. of addition, and (*b*) the Moon's interval motion, in each case:

87. 3 hours 25 minutes;   12° 47'.
88. 0 hours 37 minutes;   15° 14'.
89. 10 hours 58 minutes;   14° 58'.
90. 7 hours 11 minutes;   13° 01'.

13 Calculating the Planets' Longitudes

I am assuming that the reader will have thoroughly digested Chapter 12, and now knows how to calculate logarithms, because I want to deal with this present chapter in a straightforward way without having to go into too much explanation as we use the log. tables together.

In previous chapters we have gone through the calculation and preparation of our example case, Peter's birth-chart, to the point where the angles and the zodiacal signs have been entered relative to the house cusps. We now need to calculate the Sun's, the Moon's, and each planet's position in terms of *celestial longitude* so that these can be entered into the chart.

For this operation we need:

1. The ephemeris for the year of birth (1966).
2. The *Tables of Proportional Logarithms* (given on the back page inside the ephemeris).
3. Scrap paper on which to make our calculations, or the proper *Calculation Form A* recommended in Appendix III.
4. The birth-chart.

For Peter's birth, the necessary pages from the *1966 Ephemeris* on which are given the noon positions of the planets we shall have to refer to are reproduced in Figs. 3 and 4. We shall also need to refer to the *daily motions* of the planets for May 1966, and these can be found in Fig. 10. Finally, the *Table of Proportional Logarithms* will be found in Fig. 9.

	MAY					
D	☉	☽	♂	♀	☿	☽ dec.
	° ′ ″	° ′ ″	° ′	° ′	° ′	° ′
1	0 58 12	14 31 10	44	1 5	1 31	6 29
2	0 58 10	14 25 50	45	1 6	1 32	6 26
3	0 58 8	14 14 52	44	1 6	1 34	6 1
4	0 58 7	13 59 4	44	1 6	1 36	5 15
5	0 58 5	13 39 46	44	1 6	1 38	4 9
6	0 58 3	13 18 37	44	1 7	1 40	2 51
7	0 58 2	12 57 23	43	1 6	1 42	1 25
8	0 58 0	12 37·36	44	1 7	1 43	0 1
9	0 57 59	12 20 33	44	1 7	1 46	1 22
10	0 57 58	12 7 11	44	1 7	1 48	2 30
11	0 57 56	11 58 3	43	1 7	1 49	3 27
12	0 57 55	11 53 29	44	1 7	1 52	4 12
13	0 57 54	11 53 29	43	1 7	1 53	4 45
14	0 57 53	11 57 52	44	1 8	1 56	5 10
15	0 57 51	12 6 14	43	1 7	1 57	5 26
16	0 57 50	12 17 56	44	1 8	1 59	5 30
17	0 57 49	12 32 14	43	1 8	2 1	5 24
18	0 57 47	12 48 10	43	1 8	2 3	5 3
19	0 57 47	13 4 48	43	1 8	2 4	4 25
20	0 57 45	13 21 2	44	1 8	2 .6	3 26
21	0 57 43	13 36 1	43	1 8	2 8	2 8
22	0 57 42	13 48 58	43	1 9	2 9	0 33
23	0 57 41	13 59 24	43	1 8	2 9	1 8
24	0 57 39	14 7 4	43	1 8	2 11	2 45
25	0 57 38	14 11 54	43	1 9	2 11	4 8
26	0 57 36	14 14 3	43	1 9	2 12	5 12
27	0 57 35	14 13 37	42	1 8	2 12	5 55
28	0 57 33	14 10 42	43	1 9	2 12	6 17
29	0 57 32	14 5 23	43	1 9	2 11	6 19
30	0 57 30	13 57 38	43	1 9	2 11	6 2
31	0 57 29	13 47 27	42	1 9	2 10	5 26

Fig. 10
© W. Foulsham & Co. Ltd.

So now we are all set to calculate the Sun's, the Moon's, and each planet's position for the time of Peter's birth.

Calculating the Sun's (☉) Longitude

First we check on the *date and time* of birth in terms of G.M.T. to ensure that we use the correct data. Turning to Chapter 3, page 25, we read that:

(*a*) The G.M.T. date we must use is the 7th May.

(*b*) The G.M.T. we must use is 7.52 p.m.

The second step is to find the *interval value*. This is the interval from noon to birth, which is *7 hours 52 minutes*.

The third step is to find the log. of the interval. Referring to Fig. 9 we will find this to be *0·4844*.

The fourth step is to find the *daily motion* of the Sun on the day of birth. For this we refer to Fig. 10. But at this point we must be sure that we are using the correct figures. This is the important rule we must learn:

(a) If birth in G.M.T. is *after* noon, we look for the daily motion corresponding to the *date of birth*. This daily motion will be the distance travelled between noon on birthday to noon of the following day.

(b) If birth in G.M.T. is *before* noon, we look for the daily motion corresponding to the *day previous to that of birth*. This daily motion will be the distance travelled between noon on previous day to noon on birthday.

(c) It will be seen that in either case we always use the daily motion corresponding to the noon *prior to birth*.

Peter's birth occurred *after* noon, at 7.52 p.m. G.M.T., so turning to Fig. 10 we have to find the daily motion of the Sun corresponding to date of birthday, which is the 7th May. The date is in the first column of figures for May, and the Sun's daily motion is in the second column. Alongside the 7th May we read that the Sun's motion in longitude for the 24 hours from noon on this date is 0° 58′ 02″. You will recall that on page 101 it is stated that in the case of the Sun or Moon (the only bodies whose motion or longitude is given to seconds) when seconds are *less than 30″*, these should be ignored. *The Sun's daily motion is therefore 0° 58′.*

The fifth step is to find the log. of the daily motion. Referring to Fig. 9 we find this to be *1·3949*.

We now proceed as taught in the previous chapter, adding the log. of the interval to the log. of the daily motion, and then find the antilog.

Log. of interval   =   0·4844
Log. of Sun's motion   =   1·3949
                            ───────
  Log. of addition   =   1·8793
Antilog. of 1·8793   =   0° 19′ (Sun's motion in interval)

Now that we know the Sun's motion during the interval from noon to birth, all we have to do to find the exact longitude of the Sun *at the moment of birth* is to add the interval motion to the Sun's position at noon on birthday. We will find the Sun's position at noon on birthday (7th May) by turning to the left-hand page for the month of May in the ephemeris. This, of course, is reproduced in Fig. 3. In the fourth column in the lower portion of the page the Sun's longitude at noon for each day of the month is given. The column is headed "⊙ Long." The days of the month are given in the first column. We run our finger down this first column until we come to Peter's birth-date, the 7th. The corresponding noon position of the Sun is ♉ 16° 28′ 16″. We round this off to ♉ 16° 28′.

Sun's position noon 7th May	=	♉	16° 28′
(p.m. birth, so ADD) interval motion	=		0° 19′
Sun, at 7.52 p.m. G.M.T. 7th May	=	♉	16° 47′

Calculating the Moon's (☽) Longitude

The interval value, and the log. of the interval, will be the same for the Moon and each planet as it is for the Sun. For the Moon and each planet we have therefore simply to find their daily motion as given in Fig. 10 corresponding to birth-date (7th May), and then calculate the log. of this motion. You should now be able to find the following:

Moon's daily motion	=	12° 57′ 23″ (round off to 12° 57′)
Log. of interval	=	0·4844
Log. of Moon's motion	=	0·2679
Log. of addition	=	0·7523
Antilog. of 0·7523	=	4° 15′ (Moon's motion interval)

Turning to Fig. 3 we look for the Moon's longitude at noon on Peter's birthday, 7th May, in the same way that we looked for the Sun's position. The Moon's longitude is given in the *sixth* column. We find that it is ♐ 19° 35' 57". We round this off to ♐ 19° 36', and proceed as we did for the Sun:

Moon's position noon 7th May   =   ♐ 19° 36'
(p.m. birth, so ADD) interval motion =   4° 15'

Moon, at 7.52 p.m. G.M.T. 7th May = ♐ 23° 51'

Calculating Mercury's (☿) Longitude

The correct sequence in which we calculate the positions of the planets is according to their order (in terms of distance) from the Sun, except in the case of the Moon. The Moon being of considerable importance in the chart because of its closeness to the Earth and its speed of motion is always placed next to the Sun in importance. The planets follow in this order (though their significance and strength in an individual chart is not necessarily in this order): Mercury (☿), Venus (♀), Mars (♂), Jupiter (♃), Saturn (♄), Uranus (♅), Neptune (♆), and Pluto (♇).

Referring to Fig. 10, we find that the daily motions for Mercury are given in the *sixth* column. This is indicated by the column being headed by the symbol ☿. We will note Mercury's motion from noon on the 7th May, and then calculate the logs. as we did for the Sun and Moon, arriving at the following figures. Do you get these, too?

Mercury's daily motion   = 1° 42'
Log. of interval   = 0·4844
Log. of Mercury's motion = 1·1498

    Log. of addition   = 1·6342
Antilog. of 1·6342   = 0° 33' (Mercury's motion in interval)

We have now to find Mercury's longitude at noon on Peter's birthday, 7th May. For the Sun and Moon we referred to the left-hand page for May (Fig. 3). But in the case of the planets these will be found on the right-hand page, reproduced in Fig. 4. In the lower portion of the page the days of the month are given in the *first* column, followed by the respective columns giving the longitudes at noon for Neptune (♆), Uranus (♅), Saturn (♄), Jupiter (♃), Mars (♂), Venus (♀), and Mercury (☿). Therefore for Mercury's longitude we must refer to the *eighth* column of figures. And here is how we find Mercury's longitude at the time of Peter's birth:

Mercury's position noon 7th May	=	♈	26° 23′
(p.m. birth, so ADD) interval motion	=		0° 33′
Mercury, at 7.52 p.m. G.M.T. 7th May	=	♈	26° 56′

Did you get the same answer? Mercury is found to be in the sign Aries, because if we run our finger up the column from Mercury's position at noon on birth-date we note the symbol ♈.

Calculating Venus's (♀) Longitude

Referring to Fig. 10 we will find the daily motions for Venus in the *fifth* column.

Venus's daily motion	=	1° 06′
Log. of interval	=	0·4844
Log. of Venus's motion	=	1·3388
Log. of addition	=	1·8232
Antilog. of 1·8232	=	0° 22′ (Venus's motion in interval)

Referring to Fig. 4, and the *seventh* column in lower portion of the page, we can find the longitude for Venus at noon on the 7th May. The actual degrees and minutes are 2° 34'. With regard to the *sign* that Venus is in here is an example of how easy it is for the inexperienced student to place Venus in the *wrong* sign. If we move our eyes carefully up the column from where we have our finger-tip against 2° 34' we will note first the symbol for Aries (♈). As it is the first sign we come to in moving up the column this is the sign Venus is in: ♈ 2° 34'. The error can creep in, as I have many times known with beginner-students, if we automatically or carelessly take the *sign at the top of the column* as being that which the planet is placed in. In this case we would have erroneously given the noon position for Venus on the 7th as ♓ 2° 34'. Now we can proceed as follows:

Venus's position noon 7th May   =   ♈ 2° 34'
(p.m. birth, so ADD) interval motion   =   0° 22'
Venus, at 7.52 p.m. G.M.T. 7th May   =   ♈ 2° 56'

Calculating Mars' (♂) Longitude

Referring to Fig. 10 we will find the daily motions for Mars in the *fourth* column.

Mars' daily motion   =   0° 43'
Log. of interval   =   0·4844
Log. of Mars' motion   =   1·5249

  Log. of addition   =   2·0093
Antilog. of 2·0093   =   0° 14' (Mars' motion in interval)

Referring to Fig. 4, and the *sixth* column in lower portion of the page, we can find the longitude for Mars at noon on the 7th May:

Mars' position noon 7th May   =   ♉ 14° 33'
(p.m. birth, so ADD) interval motion =   0° 14'
Mars, at 7.52 p.m. G.M.T. 7th May   =   ♉ 14° 47'

Important Rule for a Retrograde Planet

The reader is recommended to what I have written about *retrograde* motion in both *How to Read the Ephemeris* and *The Astrologer's Astronomical Handbook*. The normal motion for a planet along the ecliptic is referred to as *direct* motion. In Fig. 4 Mercury, Venus, Mars, Jupiter and Saturn are each moving direct. But Uranus (♅) and Neptune (♆) are moving in a *retrograde* motion. This is indicated by the capital *R* directly under the sign symbols at the top of their columns. Plotted each day through the telescope these two planets would appear to be moving *backwards* in the sky, as can be verified in the ephemeris by noting the *decreasing* longitude each occupies on consecutive days.

It is a very important factor to be aware of when calculating a planet's longitude, and the following rule should be noted:

(*a*) When birth in G.M.T. occurs *after* noon, and the planet moves *direct*, interval motion is *added* to noon position.

(*b*) When birth in G.M.T. occurs *after* noon, and the planet moves *retrograde*, interval motion is *subtracted* from noon position.

(*c*) When birth in G.M.T. occurs *before* noon, and the planet moves *direct*, interval motion is *subtracted* from noon position.

(*d*) When birth in G.M.T. occurs *before* noon, and the planet moves *retrograde*, interval motion is *added* to noon position.

Calculating the Slower-Moving Planets' Longitudes

When we speak of the *slower-moving* planets we refer to Jupiter (♃), Saturn (♄), Uranus (♅), Neptune (♆), and Pluto (♇). The term speaks for itself: these planets are at such enormous distances from Earth that their daily

motions along the ecliptic in terms of longitude is notice-
ably slow compared to the motions of the planets that are
nearer to the Earth. Here is a comparison of the approximate *maximum* daily motion that can be attained by each
body:

Moon:	over 15°
Sun:	1° 01′
Mercury:	over 2°
Venus:	1° 17′
Mars:	0° 48′
Jupiter:	0° 14′
Saturn:	0° 08′
Uranus:	0° 04′
Neptune:	0° 02′
Pluto:	1½′

As will be gathered from the fact that Sun, Moon,
Mercury, Venus and Mars daily motions are conveniently
calculated in the ephemeris for quick reference (Fig. 10)
logs. are always used for finding their exact longitude for a
given time. An exception with the planets is when they
cover very little distance near their stationary points.
Generally astrologers do not use logs. for finding the
longitude of Jupiter, Saturn, Uranus, Neptune or Pluto.
We will consider Pluto presently, but with the other four
planets some astrologers simply use their noon positions,
irrespective of the birth-time. If more accuracy is desired
we can roughly estimate the planet's motion during interval
by proportion.

Personally I consider it is just as well, and efficient, to
estimate by proportion when the planet's daily motion
is 4′ or less, but to use logs. when the motion is more than
4′. It is certainly just as quick to use logs.

First, however, we must know how to find a planet's
daily motion by reference to the appropriate page of noon
positions (Fig. 4). For Jupiter we look to the *fifth* column

in lower portion of the page. As Jupiter is moving *direct*, and birth is p.m., we must subtract its longitude on the 7th from that on the 8th to find the daily motion.

Jupiter at noon 8th May   =   ♋ 0° 34′
Jupiter at noon 7th May   =   ♋ 0° 22′

Daily motion   =   0° 12′

If we wished to estimate Jupiter's *interval motion* by proportion we would say, "Jupiter's motion in 24 hours is 12′. The interval of 7 hours 52 minutes is roughly 8 hours, which is one-third of 24 hours. Therefore Jupiter's interval motion is one-third of 12′, which is 4′." But it is just as simple to use logarithms:

Log. of interval   =   0·4844
Log. of Jupiter's motion   =   2·0792

Log. of addition   =   2·5636
Antilog. of 2·5636   =   0° 04′ (Jupiter's motion in interval)
Jupiter's position noon 7th May   =   ♋ 0° 22′
(p.m. birth, so ADD) interval motion   =   0° 04′

Jupiter, at 7.52 p.m. G.M.T. 7th May   =   ♋ 0° 26′

Referring to Fig. 4 we look to the *fourth* column in lower portion of the page to find the position of Saturn at noon on the 7th May. As with each planet, we must note whether it is retrograde. Saturn moves direct in this case, so we proceed as we did for Jupiter:

Saturn at noon 8th May   =   ♓ 26° 30′
Saturn at noon 7th May   =   ♓ 26° 24′

Daily motion   =   0° 06′

Log. of interval   =   0·4844
Log. of Saturn's motion   =   2·3802
    Log. of addition   =   2·8646

Antilog. of 2·8646   =   0° 02′ (Saturn's interval
                                     motion)
Saturn's position noon 7th May   =   ♓ 26° 24′
(p.m. birth, so ADD) interval motion =   0° 02′

Saturn, at 7.52 p.m. G.M.T. 7th May =   ♓ 26° 26′

Referring to Fig. 4 we look to the *third* column in lower
portion of the page to find the position of Uranus at noon
on the 7th May. Directly under the symbol for Virgo (♍)
at the top of the column of figures we note the capital *R*,
indicating that Uranus is moving *retrograde*. So to find
this planet's daily motion we must *subtract* its longitude
at noon on the 8th May from that on the 7th May.

Uranus at noon 7th May   =   ♍ 15° 36′ *R*
Uranus at noon 8th May   =   ♍ 15° 35′ *R*
    Daily motion   =   0° 01′

As Uranus has such a small daily motion we can ignore
this and use the noon position for the 7th May.
Thus:

Uranus' position, 7.52 p.m. G.M.T. 7th May = ♍ 15° 36′ *R*

Referring to Fig. 4 we look to the *second* column in
lower portion of the page to find the position of Neptune
at noon on the 7th May. Directly under the symbol for
Scorpio (♏) at the top of the column of figures we
note the capital *R*, indicating that Neptune is moving
retrograde. So to find this planet's daily motion we proceed
as we did for Uranus, *subtracting* its longitude at noon on
the 8th May from that on the 7th May.

Neptune at noon 7th May = ♏ 20° 56′ R
Neptune at noon 8th May = ♏ 20° 54′ R

Daily motion = 0° 02′

A daily motion of 2′ is too trivial to use with logs. to find Neptune's *interval motion*, so we estimate as follows. Neptune travels 2′ in 24 hours, 1′ in 12 hours. Birth is at 7.52 p.m., which is nearer to midnight than it is to noon (being 7 hours 52 minutes from noon, 4 hours 8 minutes from midnight), therefore we estimate that Neptune's interval motion should be as for 12 hours, that is 1′.

To find Neptune's longitude *at birth* we remind ourselves that birth in G.M.T. occurs *after* noon and Neptune is *retrograde*. We therefore apply *Rule b* (page 113):

Neptune's position noon 7th May = ♏ 20° 56′ R
(subtract) Interval motion = 0° 01′

Neptune, at 7.52 p.m. G.M.T. 7th May = ♏ 20° 55′ R

THE POSITION OF PLUTO (♇) IN 1966.

Date	Long.	Lat.	Dec.	Date	Long.	Lat.	Dec.	Date	Long.	Lat.	Dec.
	° ′	° ′	° ′		° ′	° ′	° ′		° ′	° ′	° ′
Jan. 1	18 ♍26	14N 40	18N 1	May 11	15 ♍52	14N 49	19N 11	Sept. 18	18 ♍31	14N 17	17N 39
11	18 ℞20	14 45	18 8	21	15 ℞49	14 45	19 9	28	18 52	14 19	17 32
21	18 12	14 49	18 15	31	15 D48	14 41	19 5	Oct. 8	19 12	14 21	17 26
31	18 1	14 53	18 23	June 10	15 51	14 37	19 0	18	19 32	14 24	17 21
Feb. 10	17 48	14 56	18 31	20	15 57	14 33	18 54	28	19 49	14 27	17 17
20	17 34	14 58	18 39	30	16 6	14 30	18 48	Nov. 7	20 5	14 31	17 14
Mar. 2	17 18	15 0	18 46	July 10	16 17	14 26	18 40	17	20 18	14 36	17 13
12	17 2	15 1	18 53	20	16 32	14 23	18 31	27	20 28	14 41	17 14
22	16 47	15 0	18 59	30	16 49	14 20	18 23	Dec. 7	20 34	14 46	17 16
Apr. 1	16 32	14 59	19 4	Aug. 9	17 7	14 19	18 14	17	20 ℞38	14 51	17 19
11	16 19	14 58	19 8	19	17 27	14 17	18 5	27	20 38	14 56	17 24
21	16 7	14 55	19 10	29	17 48	14 17	17 56	Jan. 1	20 37	14 59	17 ℞26
May 1	15 58	14 52	19 11	Sept. 8	18 9	14 17	17 47				

Fig. 11

Calculating Pluto's (♇) *Longitude*

The position of Pluto for every *tenth* day in 1966 is given on page 39 in *Raphael's 1966 Ephemeris*, and these are reproduced in Fig. 11. Pluto's positions each year have appeared in this form since 1940.

To find Pluto's position on a given date this can only be done by proportion, unless the date happens to coincide with one of the dates shown in the table. This table is quite easy to read. In the first column is the *date*; in the second column headed "Long." is the corresponding *longitude*; in the third column headed "Lat." is the corresponding *latitude* (which we do not use); in the fourth column is the corresponding *declination*, indicated by the heading "Dec.", which we will apply in Chapter 15.

A point not previously brought to the notice of students until I mentioned it in Chapter 11 of *How to Read the Ephemeris* concerns the *stationary points* indicated for Pluto. The *R* against a date generally means a planet is then stationary before moving in a retrograde direction; the *D* against a date means the planet is stationary and about to move in a direct motion again. But with Pluto the actual date these letters are placed against is not necessarily the exact date when Pluto is stationary. Since 1939 the times and dates of Pluto's stations or stationary points have been given in the section of the ephemeris entitled *A Complete Aspectarian*. For instance, in Fig. 11 the *D* against the 31st May might seem to imply that on that date Pluto is stationary, about to turn direct. But this actually occurs at 9.36 a.m. on the 27th May. The discrepancy is unavoidable because of positions only being given for each tenth day.

Peter's birth-date is 7th May. Referring to Fig. 11 we find that this date falls between the given dates of 1st May and 11th May. So we have to estimate by proportion the approximate position of Pluto on the 7th May. Note that Pluto is retrograde, therefore we subtract the longitude for the *later* date from the longitude for the *earlier* date.

Pluto's longitude for 1st May	=	♍ 15° 58′ *R*
Pluto's longitude for 11th May	=	♍ 15° 52′ *R*
Pluto's motion in 10 days	=	0° 06′

Pluto's motion in 10 days is a mere 6′. What we have to do is find its motion in *1 day*, then multiply this number by the number of days separating the earlier date (1st May) and the birth-date (7th May). Actually, for a mere 6′ motion this simple calculation is hardly necessary, but it is best that you learn how to do it for cases when Pluto's motion in 10 days is larger. To divide by 10 is simply a matter of putting in a decimal point. Thus:

6′ motion divided by 10 (days) = 0·6′ motion in 1 day. Number of days between earlier date (1st May) and birth-date (7th May) = 6 days.
To find Pluto's motion during these 6 days, multiply the daily motion (0·6′) by 6 (days) = 3·6′ (round off to 4′). If Pluto were moving *direct*, these 4′ would be *added* to the longitude given against the earlier date (1st May). As Pluto is *retrograde*, these 4′ must be *subtracted* from the longitude given against the earlier date:

Pluto's longitude 1st May	=	♍ 15° 58′ *R*
Motion from 1st–7th May	=	0° 04′
Pluto's longitude 7th May	=	♍ 15° 54′ *R*

Here is another example, for when Pluto is moving less slowly and in a direct motion. What is Pluto's longitude on the 26th August 1966? We will refer to Fig. 11 again:

Pluto's longitude 29th August	=	♍ 17° 48′
Pluto's longitude 19th August	=	♍ 17° 27′
Pluto's motion in 10 days	=	0° 21′

Pluto's motion in 1 day = 0° 21′ ÷ 10 = 2·1′.

Number of days between earlier date (19th August) and given date (26th August) = 7 days.

To find Pluto's motion during these 7 days = 2·1' (daily motion) × 7 (days) = 14·7' (round off to 15').

To find Pluto's longitude on given date, 26th August:

Pluto's longitude 19th August   =   ♍ 17° 27'

(Plus) Motion 19th–26th August =   15'

Pluto's longitude 26th August   =   ♍ 17° 42'

Calculating the Moon's Nodes

The two points in the Moon's orbit where it intersects the plane of the ecliptic (plane of the Earth's path around the Sun) are called the *nodes*. Astrologers differ in their opinions as to the significance of these points in the ecliptic, but they are still generally entered in charts. Here is an opportunity for an enthusiastic young astrologer to test their validity by studying their possible significance in four or five thousand charts.

- ☊ *Ascending node*, where the Moon crosses ecliptic from south to north.
- ☋ *Descending node*, where the Moon crosses ecliptic from north to south.

The positions of the nodes in terms of longitude are to be found in the *eighth* column at the top of the right-hand page for each month in *Raphael's Ephemeris*, as can be seen in Fig. 4. Longitude is in degrees (°) and minutes (') and is given only for the ascending or north node. The longitude of the descending or south node is always the exact opposite point in the ecliptic to that occupied by the north node. Longitude is given for alternate days, and to find the longitude for an intermediate date to any two given one simply takes the midpoint between these two.

We will find the longitude of the north node for Peter's chart. Birth-date is the 7th May. In the first column at the

top of Fig. 4 alternate dates of the month are given. The
fourth line down is the 7th. So if you read off the longitude
for the fourth line down in the node's column you will get
Taurus (♉) 25° 57′. The symbol for Taurus is given
alongside the longitude for the first day of the month in the
node's column.

It should be noted that the node's motion is retrograde,
the longitude decreasing each day by about 3′. Generally
the noon position for the north node is used, whatever the
time of birth. If accuracy is desired, I suggest that (a) if
birth G.M.T. is 8 p.m. or after, subtract 1′ from node's
noon position, and (b) if birth G.M.T. is between 0.00 a.m.
to 4.00 a.m., add 1′ to node's noon position.

We have said that the south node's longitude is the
opposite point in the ecliptic to the longitude of the north
node. We can now write down these points as they apply
to Peter's chart:

   ☊ North node: ♉ 25° 56′
   ☋ South node: ♍ 25° 56′

Most students will probably notice right away that we
have subtracted 1′ from the nodes' noon positions,
because Peter's birth is around 8 p.m. G.M.T.

When Daily Motion Has To Be Calculated

Prior to 1905 the convenient listing of daily motions (as
in Fig. 10) do not appear in *Raphael's Ephemeris*. This
means that the daily motions have to be calculated by
subtracting the longitude at noon prior to birth from the
longitude at noon of following day. This can sometimes
pose a problem for beginner-students, particularly where
it involves a change of sign. There are two methods by
which this subtraction can be made and understood, and
the student can make his own choice. Here with an example
is *Method A*.

What is the Moon's daily motion from noon 12th May 1966?

Moon's longitude noon 13th May	=	♓	3° 30' 12"
Moon's longitude noon 12th May	=	♒	21° 36' 43"
	Daily motion	=	11° 53' 29"

The student may ask, "How can one subtract a greater number from a lesser number?" This is how we do it. To subtract 43" from 12" cannot be done without "borrowing" *one whole minute* or 60". These 60" are added to the 12" in the top line, making a total of 72". We can now subtract 43" from 72" = 29". As we have "borrowed" 1' from the 30' shown in the top line, we are 1' short, which leaves 29'—from which we have to subtract a greater number again, 36'. So once again we "borrow", this time it is *one whole degree* or 60'. These 60' are added to the 29' remaining in the top line. It is then a simple matter subtracting 36' from 89' (60' + 29' = 89'). The answer is 53'. Now we move to the degrees. We have "borrowed" 1°, so this leaves only 2° now in the top line, from which we have to subtract a greater number again, 21°! This time we "borrow" *one whole sign* or 30°, and add these to the 2° in the top line, making a total of 32°. We can now subtract 21° from 32°, leaving 11°.

Method B is this. We first subtract the lesser longitude from one whole sign or 30° when there is a change of sign involved as with the example figures we have just used. As follows:

One whole sign	=	30° 00' 00"
Moon's longitude noon 12th May	= (♒)	21° 36' 43"
		8° 23' 17"

We cannot subtract 43" from 00" so we "borrow" *one whole minute* or 60". 43" subtracted from 60" leaves 17". Moving to the minutes column, we have "borrowed" 1' so this leaves not 00′ or 60′ that would have to be "borrowed", but 59′ in the top line. This is arrived at by "borrowing" 60′ (because we cannot subtract 36′ from 00′) and then having to subtract 1′ that we have already "borrowed" from the minutes column. So, we subtract 36′ from 59′ = 23′. With the degrees column the subtraction is straightforward. We had "borrowed" 1°, leaving 29° in the top column, from which we subtract 21°, leaving 8°. The second stage in this calculation is to *add* the answer we have just arrived at to the Moon's position on the following day, for the 13th May. Thus:

Moon's longitude noon
13th May   = (♓) 3° 30′ 12″
            ADD =   8° 23′ 17″
      Daily motion =   11° 53′ 29″ (rounded off
                                to 11° 53′)

Latitude

Although the ephemeris gives the planets' and the Moon's positions in terms of *latitude* (measurement north or south of the ecliptic) these are not normally used by the astrologer. The student can therefore ignore these columns of figures, unless of course he or she hears of a system of chart construction that makes use of latitude. An extremely interesting system devised by Norman Blunsdon, D.F.Astrol.S., that he calls the *3D Celestial Birth Map*, is designed to show the plotted positions of the planets' latitudes. This chart is a probable significant breakthrough into a new dimension of chart construction, and warrants intensive study and testing by interested students.

Exercises

The answers to these exercises can be found in Appendix VII.

Calculate the positions of the Sun, Moon, planets, and Moon's nodes for the following:

91. A birth at 10.38 p.m. G.M.T., 5th May 1966.
92. A birth at 1.22 a.m. G.M.T., 18th May 1966.

14 *Entering the Planets in the Chart*

In the previous chapter we calculated the positions of the Sun, Moon, planets, and Moon's nodes. If, when calculating these factors for a chart, you do not use a printed form such as the Calculation Form A recommended in Appendix III, but use scrap paper, the best idea is to list the planets according to the sign each is in. You would first write down the signs in their correct sequence beginning with Aries, Taurus and through to Pisces. Planets are then entered under the respective sign their calculated position shows them to be in. Working to a method in this way makes it simpler and more efficient for you to enter the planets in the chart.

This is how your list of planets and nodes for Peter's chart should now appear:

♀ Venus:	♈	2° 56'
☿ Mercury:	♈	26° 56'
♂ Mars:	♉	14° 47'
☉ Sun:	♉	16° 47'
☊ North Node:	♉	25° 56'
♃ Jupiter:	♋	0° 26'
♅ Uranus:	♍	15° 36' *R*
♇ Pluto:	♍	15° 54' *R*
♆ Neptune:	♏	20° 55' *R*
☋ South Node:	♏	25° 56'
☽ Moon:	♐	23° 51'
♄ Saturn:	♓	26° 26'

The average student has only to erect a few charts to

"get the hang of things". The important rules to observe imply that the erection of a chart, so that it is pleasant to read and there is no risk of misinterpretation of symbols and figures, is just a case of applying common sense and method—plus an innate desire to give the impression of efficiency.

The important rules I would give priority to are:

1. Make up your mind that each chart you erect is going to reflect the measure of your efficiency and knowledge as an astrologer.
2. Draw the planets' symbols bold, clear, easy-to-read-at-a-glance.
3. Keep the planets' symbols *upright*. A common fault is to twist the chart around as each planet is entered. This way the symbols can be on their side, upside down, and annoyingly confusing to read. The way to avoid doing this is not to move the chart-form, keep it upright in front of you as you enter the planets.
4. Don't enter each planet direct into the chart as soon as you calculate its position. List each planet methodically as already mentioned, and only start entering in the chart when *all* factors have been calculated. If you enter each planet haphazardly you may find that where you have entered two planets close together a third planet has now to be entered *between* them, which is impossible. You then have to place this third planet out of line with the rest near the centre of the chart, where it will become muddled up with the aspect-lines you will presently enter. For example, referring to Fig. 7, let us say that ⊙ and ♂ have been entered as shown in ♉, quite haphazardly. Then we calculate Jupiter's position, for this example we will say ♉ 15° 18′—only to find there is no space in which to squeeze Jupiter between Sun and Mars!
5. Always place the planets close to the rim of the chart

as shown in Fig. 7, with the degrees and minutes of their position nearer and in line with the centre of the chart. This gives an impression of efficiency and method, as much as does neatness.

6. Always allow a reasonable space in the middle of the chart for entering the aspect-lines that you will learn to do in Chapter 16. Aspect-lines will then not become confused with figures and planets' symbols.

7. As you enter each planet, make a small line or dot linking it with the sign it is placed in, as has been done in Fig. 7. Especially where several planets are bunched together this ensures that it is clear to anyone which sign each planet is in.

8. Do remember that just as you will always enter the signs in their correct sequence in an *anti-clockwise* direction, so do the planets move in this same direction. Therefore be careful that you enter a planet on the correct side of a house cusp, or if it is at the beginning or end of a sign that you place it at the correct end!

Now to enter the planets in Peter's chart. This has already been done in Fig. 7, but you will also want to complete the chart that you have been doing step by step throughout the chapters we worked through together. This is the best way to learn: to do the job yourself, and not just be shown how.

The reason for listing planets according to the sign each is in will now become clear. We start with Aries (♈). There are two planets in this sign, Venus (♀) and Mercury (☿). We enter Venus first as it has the smaller longitude, 2° 56'. But don't be hasty . . . look at your list first to see whether there is a planet or perhaps planets in the latter degrees of Pisces (♓). This is where *Rule 4* becomes evident. You may enter Venus at the beginning of Aries and then find you have left no space between the symbol ♀ and the 5th house cusp for a planet placed towards the end of Pisces to be entered. As it happens there *is* another planet that needs to be entered between ♀ and the 5th house cusp: it is Saturn (♄) in ♓ 26° 26′. So we carefully enter ♀ and the degrees and minutes of its position just as illustrated in Fig. 7, making a small mark against the sign ♈. And we leave room for ♄ to be entered presently.

Next we enter ☿ towards the other end of ♈. The next sign is Taurus (♉), and three factors have to be entered against this sign: ♂ in 14° 47′, ☉ in 16° 47′, and ☊ in 25° 56′. Here again we need to be careful. It is best to enter ☉ first because it is placed nearer than ♂ to the 7th house cusp. Then we enter ♂, remembering to make that small mark to clearly indicate the sign each planet is in. And so we go on, sign by sign, until every factor is entered correctly in the chart as in Fig. 7.

It is not being fussy to try to make a tidy and methodical job of charting. From my own experience I know what a beneficial impression a well-presented natal chart has on a client or on anyone who has cause to look at it. Too many professional astrologers I regret to say turn out shabby, confused, unbusinesslike charts, in which figures are often illegible, and therefore mistakes could be made in reading planets' positions. This is the kind of astrology the unenlightened critics of the subject would expect to find and associate with the fortune-telling gypsy at the end of the pier. It is this kind of impression and image of the astrologer that the teaching of the Faculty of Astrological Studies helps to dispel.

Entering Planets in Placidus System Chart

The houses of the Placidus chart are of varying size, as can be seen by noting the distance between degrees on successive cusps. Therefore the planets do not need to be entered in the chart in quite the same way as for the Equal House System, that is by trying to place each as near as possible to the actual degree it occupies. *With Placidus charting a planet is entered as close as possible to the house cusp on which is the sign the planet is in.*

It is difficult enough as it is to read a Placidus chart quickly and note the aspects between planets because the signs are not placed evenly as in the Equal House System. But too often one comes upon a Placidus chart where it would be so easy to misread the sign-placing of a planet due to the confused and unmethodical manner in which the planets have been entered.

Have a look at Fig. 8, Peter's chart erected to the Placidus System. Note how a planet in an *intercepted* sign is clearly indicated to be in that sign by the neat bracketing of sign and planet. Note how ♄ and ♀ in the 4th house are not thrown together but each placed near to the house cusp where the sign it is in is placed. In this way we know at a glance that they are in different signs, without having to confirm this by noting their degree positions.

The *angles* in the Placidus chart are, of course, "fixed". They are the horizontal line defined by the 1st and 7th house cusps; and the vertical line defined by the 4th and 10th house cusps.

15 Calculating the Planets' Declinations

Declination is the measured distance of a planet north or south of the *celestial equator*. The *celestial* equator is the term used for the plane of the *terrestrial* equator when it is extended into the celestial sphere or infinity.

Not all astrologers bother with calculating declinations, but generally this is done, though opinions as to the significance of declination angles differ. The purpose of finding the planets' positions in terms of declination as accurately as possible is because the *parallel* aspect (see Chapter 16) derives from these. The equator is a very significant feature of the Earth's sphere in its relation to both the Sun and Moon in the strictly physical sense, and parallel aspects used in conjunction with longitudinal aspects have been found frequently to correlate with outstanding factors in the life of an individual. There is need for much research in this direction, meanwhile it is as well to calculate declinations for all the more important charts the student erects.

The position of the Sun in declination at noon G.M.T. for any given day during May 1966 will be found in Fig. 3, in the *fifth* column in lower portion of the page. Measurement is in degrees (°) and minutes ('), as indicated by these symbols at the head of the column. The capital *N* in the middle of the top line, against the 1st of the month, implies that the Sun is *north* of the Earth's equator, in declination north. The capital *S* in the declination column means the body is *south* of the equator. Be careful to note whether declination changes from north to south or from south to north. This will be indicated by this letter symbol being inserted at the appropriate date somewhere down the column. The Sun, of course, changes declination only twice a year, at the equinoxes, therefore we would not expect to find a change indicated for the Sun during May.

The Moon's position at noon G.M.T. in declination is also given in Fig. 3, in the *eighth* column in lower portion of the page. Be sure that you do not mistake the Moon's declination shown in the *last* column for the noon position. This last column gives the Moon's declination for *midnight*.

The declinations of the planets Mercury and Venus are given in the top section of Fig. 4 for noon G.M.T. each day. The declinations for Mars, Jupiter, Saturn, Uranus and Neptune are shown in the top section of Fig. 3. Note that positions for Mars are given for noon G.M.T. for each day of the month, whereas for the other four planets these are given only for noon G.M.T. on alternate days, since these planets move but slowly in terms of declination. Pluto's declinations are given in Fig. 11 in the fourth, eighth, and twelfth columns, for every tenth day.

In the same way that we calculated the exact longitude with the use of logarithms in Chapter 13 so do we use these time-saving logs. for the calculation of declination.

Rule for Increasing and Decreasing Declination

It is very important to note whether declination is *increasing* or *decreasing*. We speak of declination increasing when a body is moving away from the equator in the direction of its ultimate maximum declination position. Declination decreases when a body is returning from maximum declination towards the equator.

As an example, referring to Fig. 3, the Moon is seen to have crossed the equator from south to north declination prior to noon on the 16th May 1966. We can tell this is so by noting in the eighth column in lower section of the page that at noon the Moon's declination is 0° N. 16', which

means it is just 16′ north of the equator at noon. At noon
the next day (17th) declination has *increased* to 5° 46′,
and by noon on the 18th it has increased further to 11° 10′.
Each successive day declination increases until by noon
on the 23rd May a maximum is attained, 26° 45′. The
expression then is that Moon is "at maximum declination
north". Sometimes it is not clear which of two days the
Moon attains maximum declination when the figures given
are the same or almost so. One can easily ascertain on
which day maximum declination occurs by turning to the
section in the ephemeris entitled *Phenomena* (usually
around page 29). As a point of interest, maximum declination north in the above case was reached by the Moon at
7.59 a.m. E.T. on the 23rd May, when maximum was
26° 47′. Thus, by noon on that same day declination had
already begun to decrease by 2′ as the Moon began its
descent towards the equator. We can follow this descent
each day between 24th–29th May through the decreasing
figures.

Here is the very important rule the student must always
remember to refer to when calculating declination, whether
it concerns the Sun, Moon, or a planet, until he is able to
remember what to do by practice and experience.

(*a*) When birth G.M.T. occurs *before* noon, and
declination is *increasing*, the interval motion in
declination must be *subtracted* from noon position.

(*b*) When birth G.M.T. occurs *before* noon, and declination is *decreasing*, the interval motion in declination
must be *added* to noon position.

(*c*) When birth G.M.T. occurs *after* noon, and declination is *increasing*, the interval motion in declination
must be *added* to noon position.

(*d*) When birth G.M.T. occurs *after* noon, and declination is *decreasing*, the interval motion in declination
must be *subtracted* from noon position.

Calculating the Sun's (☉) Declination

For the calculations that will now be done together we will use the positions applicable to Peter's chart, whose birth-date we remind ourselves is the 7th May. We will also make a note that as his time of birth is 7.52 p.m. G.M.T. the interval value or period from noon to birth is 7 hours 52 minutes. In Chapter 13 we calculated the log. of this interval to be *0·4844.*

Referring to the *fifth* column in lower section of the page (Fig. 3) we write down the following:

Sun's declination noon 8th May	=	17° 02′ N.
Sun's declination noon 7th May	=	16° 46′ N.
Daily motion	=	0° 16′

As we know from the calculations we did in Chapter 13, the Sun's daily motion is arrived at by subtracting the lesser declination from the greater declination, the lesser in this case being for the 7th May. And on to the next step, just as we did when finding the exact *longitude* for the Sun:

Log. of interval	=	0·4844
Log. of Sun's motion	=	1·9542
Log. of Addition	=	2·4386
Antilog. of 2·4386	=	0° 05′ (Sun's interval motion)

Here is when we note whether the Sun's declination is increasing or decreasing. It is increasing, and as birth is *after* noon we must observe *Rule C* (page 132), and *add* interval motion to noon position.

Sun's declination noon 7th May	=	16° 46′ N.
Interval motion in declination	=	0° 05′
Sun, at 7.52 p.m. G.M.T.	=	16° 51′ N.

Calculating the Moon's (☽) *Declination*

Referring to the *eighth* column in lower section of Fig. 3 we write down the following:

Moon's declination noon 8th May　=　26° 37' S.
Moon's declination noon 7th May　=　25° 12' S,

　　　　　　　　Daily motion　=　 1° 25'

As the moon travels over 6° in declination when around the equator, a far greater distance than any of the other bodies, its daily motion in declination is conveniently calculated for the astrologer for each day of the year on pages 26–28 in *Raphael's Ephemeris*. We are thus able to check the daily motion we have just calculated, by referring to Fig. 10. In the *seventh* column, headed " ☽ dec.", for the 7th May we read that the daily motion in declination is 1° 25'.

Log. of interval　　　　=　0·4844
Log. of Moon's motion　=　1·2289

　　Log. of addition　=　1·7133
Antilog. of 1·7133　　=　0° 28'　(Moon's interval
　　　　　　　　　　　　　　　　　 motion)

Is the Moon's declination increasing or decreasing? By comparing its declination at noon on the 7th and noon on the 8th it is evident that it is *increasing*. As birth is *after* noon we observe *Rule C* (page 132), and *add* interval motion to noon position.

Moon's declination noon 7th May　=　25° 12' S.
Interval motion in declination　　=　 0° 28'

Moon, at 7.52 p.m. G.M.T.　　　=　25° 40' S.

Calculating Mercury's (☿) *Declination*

Referring to the *sixth* and *seventh* columns at the top of Fig. 4 we can read Mercury's position in declination for each day of May. The first of these two columns gives declinations on uneven dates, the second column gives these on even dates. The *N* at the top of each column tells us that declination is *north* of the equator.

Mercury's declination noon 8th May = 8° 36' N.
Mercury's declination noon 7th May = 7° 55' N.

                Daily motion = 0° 41'

Log. of interval   = 0·4844
Log. of Mercury's motion = 1·5456

      Log. of addition = 2·0300
Antilog. of 2·0300   = 0° 13' (Mercury's interval
                            motion)

It will, I'm sure, be clear to every reader that on the 7th May Mercury's declination is *increasing*, and as birth is *after* noon we observe *Rule C* once again:

Mercury's declination noon 7th May = 7° 55' N.
Interval motion in declination   = 0° 13'

Mercury, at 7.52 p.m. G.M.T.   = 8° 08' N.

Calculating Venus's (♀) Declination

Referring to the *third* and *fourth* columns at the top of Fig. 4 we can read the positions in declination for Venus for noon on each day of May. The two columns are arranged similarly to those for Mercury. At the top of each column, alongside declination for the 1st and 2nd days of the month is the letter *S*, indicating that Venus is *south* of the equator. But here is an interesting difference to the figures we have dealt with so far. Between the 1st and 7th declination is *decreasing*. And then on the 8th and 9th we get this:

Venus declination 8th May = 0° N. 7'
Venus declination 9th May = 0° N. 31'

The appearance of *N* against declination for 8th May means that declination has changed from south to north. This indication is necessarily repeated in the adjoining column for the 9th May. To find the daily motion in declination of Venus for the 24 hours from noon 7th May we must add together the *17' south declination* and the *7' north declination*. For this reason:

Between 1st and 7th May it is clear that declination is *decreasing*. At some time before noon on the 8th May declination changes from south to north, and by noon on that day it has *increased* to 0° 07' north. Thus, between noon 7th May and noon 8th May Venus covers 24' in declination in this way:

Decreasing through 0° 17' S. to 0° 00' (on equator)
Increasing through 0° 00' to 0° 07' N.

This is a point one needs to be careful about when a planet or the Sun or Moon are crossing the equator. Here is another example, this time in the Moon's case:

Moon's declination noon 29th May 1966 =   1° 20' N.
Moon's declination noon 30th May 1966 =   4° 59' S.

Daily motion =   6° 19'

Do you see why we need to ADD the declination given for each day? We are adding 1° 20' of *north* declination covered by the Moon, and 4° 59' of *south* declination it also covers, in the period of 24 hours. This is confirmed by reference to Fig. 10. Moon's daily motion in declination from noon 29th May is shown as 6° 19'.

We now proceed with declination for Venus.

Venus's declination noon 7th May =   0° 17' S. ⎫
Venus's declination noon 8th May =   0° 07' N. ⎬ add
                                                 ⎭

Daily motion =   0° 24'

Log. of interval   =   0·4844
Log. of Venus's motion =   1·7781

    Log. of addition   =   2·2625
Antilog. of 2·2625   =   0° 08′ (Venus's interval mo-
                                            tion)

As at noon on the 7th May declination of Venus is *decreasing*, and birth occurs *after* noon, we must observe *Rule D* (page 132), and *subtract* the interval motion from noon position on the 7th.

Venus's declination noon 7th May = 0° 17′ S.
(subtract) Interval motion   = 0° 08′

Venus, at 7.52 p.m. G.M.T.   = 0° 09′ S.

This would be an apt moment to describe another situation the astrologer needs to understand, similar to the above. We will assume that the declination for Venus on the 7th May had been 0° 05′ S., and on the 8th it had been 0° 20′ N. We will also assume that the interval motion for Venus had been 0° 10′. To find the declination for Venus at the given birth-time we would first subtract the 5′ of south declination from the 10′ of interval motion, which would leave 5′ of interval motion. This remaining 5′ would represent 5′ of increase in *north* declination, from 0° 00′ (equator) to 0° 05′ N. This then would be the declination we are looking for: 0° 05′ N.

Calculating Mars' (♂) Declination

Referring to the *eleventh* and *twelfth* columns at the top of Fig. 3 we can read the positions in declination for Mars for noon on each day of May. The two columns are arranged similar to those for Mercury and Venus. See if you can now follow the straightforward calculations for Mars:

Mars' declination noon 8th May = 16° 19′ N.
Mars' declination noon 7th May = 16° 05′ N.

Daily motion = 0° 14′

Log. of interval   = 0·4844
Log. of Mars' motion = 2·0122

Log. of addition = 2·4966
Antilog. of 2·4966   = 0° 05′ (Mars' interval motion)
Mars' declination noon 7th May = 16° 05′ N.
Mars' interval motion   = 0° 05′

Mars, at 7.52 p.m. G.M.T.   = 16° 10′ N.

Calculating the Slow-Moving Planets' Declinations

Declination positions for Jupiter, Saturn, Uranus and Neptune are listed for alternate days of the month at the top of Fig. 3. Jupiter's declination does not change between 7th and 9th May, therefore we can list it for Peter's birth at 23° 24′ N. For Saturn:

Saturn's declination noon 7th May = 3° 16′ S.
Saturn's declination noon 9th May = 3° 12′ S.

Saturn's motion in TWO days = 0° 04′

If Saturn travels 4′ in *two* days, by proportion we estimate that it travels 4′ divided by 2=2′ in *one* day or 24 hours. In 12 hours (equal to period from noon to midnight on 7th May) it would travel 1′. Therefore, as 7.52 p.m. (Peter's birth-time) is nearer to *midnight* than it is to noon, we would say that the interval motion for Saturn is roughly 1′. As Saturn is decreasing in declination we will subtract this 1′ from its noon position on the 7th May. Thus, 3° 16′ S. minus 1′=3° 15′ S., or Saturn's declination at Peter's birth.

The declinations for Uranus and Neptune we can easily assess:

Uranus: declination for Peter's birth =   6° 25' N.
Neptune: declination for Peter's birth =   16° 15' S.

There now remains only the declination for Pluto. Turning to Fig. 11 we note:

Pluto's declination 1st May   =   19° 11' N.
Pluto's declination 11th May   =   19° 11' N.
Pluto's declination on 7th May is therefore 19° 11' N.

The Ascendant and Midheaven Declinations

Rarely does the present-day astrologer use the declination for the Ascendant or the Midheaven. As Tutor to students from nearly seventy countries throughout the world I have, however, been asked many times to explain how one can find the declinations for these two angles of the chart.

The method is quite simple. First you write down the longitude of the Ascendant and Midheaven:

Peter's Ascendant = ♏ 20° 19'
Peter's Midheaven = ♍ 10° 26'

The idea is to find when the Sun is in approximately the same degree of longitude. An approximation is all that is required, though Virgoan students may wish to compute the declination exactly! We pick up an ephemeris (for any year will do). We will use the 1966 ephemeris. When we have found the Sun's approximate longitude to the above, the Sun's *corresponding declination* will be approximately that of Peter's Ascendant and Midheaven respectively. Looking through the ephemeris for 1966 we find:

13th November 1966 Sun's longitude at noon is ♏ 20° 39'. The corresponding declination is 17° 55' S.
3rd September 1966 Sun's longitude at noon is ♍ 10° 32'. The corresponding declination is 7° 37' N.
Therefore, Peter's Ascendant's declination is 17° 55' S.
               Peter's Midheaven's declination is 7° 37' N.

Listing the Declinations

The recommended chart-forms (Appendix III) have a column in which the planets' declinations may be entered. This is the order in which they will appear on the form (ignoring the declinations for Ascendant and M.C.) for Peter's birth:

	Declination
☉	16° 51′ N.
☽	25° 40′ S.
☿	8° 08′ N.
♀	0° 09′ S.
♂	16° 10′ N.
♃	23° 24′ N.
♄	3° 15′ S.
♅	6° 25′ N.
♆	16° 15′ S.
♇	19° 11′ N.

Exercises

The answers to these exercises can be found in Appendix VII.

Calculate the Moon's declination, using the following data:

93. Birth 2nd May 1966, at 4.30 a.m. G.M.T.
94. Birth 6th May 1966, at 8.23 p.m. G.M.T.
95. Birth 25th May 1966, at 10.15 a.m. G.M.T.
96. Birth 29th May 1966, at 9.20 p.m. G.M.T.

Calculate the declination for the Sun, Venus, and Mars, using the following data:

97. Birth 9th May 1966, at 5.15 p.m. G.M.T.
98. Birth 12th May 1966, at 1.00 a.m. G.M.T.
99. Birth 20th May 1966, at noon G.M.T.
100. Birth 27th May 1966, at 7.15 a.m. G.M.T.

16 *The Aspects*

When we speak of an *aspect* between two planets we are referring to a particular angular measurement along the ecliptic in terms of longitude separating these two bodies, as viewed from the Earth.

In this book we are concerned essentially with the construction of the natal chart, therefore no attempt will be made to discuss the aspects from the interpretational viewpoint.

Mention must be made of the classification of aspects into two types, *major* or *minor*, because the major aspects are allowed a wider *orb* than is the case with the minor aspects. An *orb* is an allowance of a certain number of degrees either side of an exact aspect. This means that even though two planets are not forming an *exact* aspect, they can still be said to form that aspect if the distance separating them falls within the limits of the orb the aspect is allowed. This will be explained and clearly understood when we work on examples.

The student will read astrological textbooks by different authors and will find that opinions differ just a little regarding the orbs in some cases. The orbs we will apply are those recommended by The Mayo School of Astrology. The only aspect on which Margaret Hone, author of *The Modern Textbook of Astrology*, and myself differ as to its orb is the *sextile*. Margaret Hone suggests 4° orb, I personally use 6°.

Numerous aspects have been devised by astrologers, based mostly on the division of the circle of 360° by one of the numerals, 2, 3, 4, 5, 6, 8, 10, 12. For example, the divisors 2, 4, and 8 produce aspects that tend to *disharmony*:

the *opposition* (180°), the *square* (90°), and the *semi-square* (45°). The divisors 3, 6, and 12 produce aspects that tend to *harmony* and *ease* of expression: the *trine* (120°), the *sextile* (60°), and the *semi-sextile* (30°). I would agree with Charles Carter that "all multiples of 15° produce valid aspects". But considering that these alone provide 24 different aspects, and no significant research to test the validity of *all* these fifteenth-degrees has ever been done, I would prefer to confine my teaching in this chapter to the following aspects:

			Orb	Aspect-limits
☌	0°	conjunction	8°	0°– 8°
⚺	30°	semi-sextile	2°	28°– 32°
∠	45°	semi-square	2°	43°– 47°
✶	60°	sextile	6°	54°– 66°
□	90°	square	8°	82°– 98°
△	120°	trine	8°	112°–128°
⚼	135°	sesquiquadrate	2°	133°–137°
⚻	150°	quincunx	2°	148°–152°
☍	180°	opposition	8°	172°–180°

Aspect-Patterns

In Fig. 7 the planets in many cases are seen to be linked by lines, which we refer to as *aspect-lines*. These lines convey at a glance all the aspects formed by the planets, and the trained astrologer recognizes various *aspect-patterns* that he associates with particular behavioural-patterns. These are formed by certain groupings of planets inter-related by aspects, and a few of the more important of these patterns are mentioned in Chapter 17.

In Fig. 7, the heavier lines link any two planets forming a *difficult* or *disharmonious major aspect*. The usual practice is to draw these lines in *blue* or *black* ink, but for the purpose of this illustration they are shown as heavy lines. The thinner unbroken lines link any two planets forming an *harmonious major aspect*, and in practice these are normally drawn in *red* ink. The broken lines link any two planets forming a *minor aspect*, whether these are "weakly harmonious" or "weakly disharmonious" types.

Aspect-lines are not normally entered in charts set up to the Placidus House System. The reason being that the planets are not placed around the chart as near as possible to the actual degrees they occupy, as in the Equal House chart; also, the size of the houses can be so distorted that any aspect-pattern would also tend to be distorted.

The student should be *methodical* in entering the aspect-lines, otherwise he will finish up with a dreadfully confused mess, with lines running through planets' symbols and figures. It is important that the planets are first entered alongside each other where they are grouped together, and not placed in a bundle so that two could be in the same direct line with the centre of the chart—otherwise it will not be possible to tell which aspect-line is intended for which planet! The very best method is to obtain a pair of compasses with a pencil in one end, or a pair of dividers. Stick one point in the centre of the chart, and then carefully set the other point so that at the *same distance from the chart-centre* a tiny "dot" can be placed against each planet. It is then a simple matter of using a ruler to join any two dots with the correct type of line where the two planets are in aspect.

Finding the Aspects

Astrologers may differ in the way they go about finding aspects between planets, but whatever the method the student may prefer as he becomes accomplished at chart-construction he must always be *methodical* so that there is no risk of overlooking an aspect.

In Fig. 12 the aspects are shown for our example case, Peter's chart. This is how we tabulate the aspects. For instance, the Sun is shown in conjunction (☌) with Mars. This can be found by noting what has been entered in the

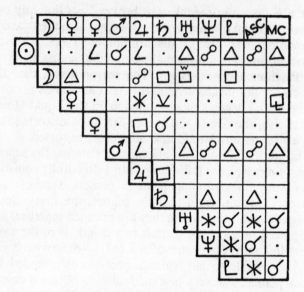

Fig. 12. Aspects for Peter's chart.

square at the intersection of the horizontal line for the Sun (☉) and the vertical column for Mars (♂). As can be seen, a planet will rarely form an aspect with *all* the other planets. The Sun forms six aspects: ☉ ∠♀, ☉ ☌ ♂, ☉∠♃, ☉△♅, ☉ ☍♆, ☉△♇.

I want you to make your own copy of Fig. 12 but do not enter the aspects yet. As each is found you can enter these in the appropriate square, but do not refer to Fig. 12 until all possible aspects have been found. Then check with Fig. 12 and compare the tabulated aspects with your own. The most efficient method is to enter the aspect's symbol in the appropriate square as you find it, and at the same time draw in the *aspect-line* linking the two planets forming the aspect. *If the two planets do not form an aspect you should put a tiny dot in the square, which tells you that you have checked these two planets and no aspect is formed.*

When looking for aspects there are two things to remember. First, longitude is measured around the chart in an *anticlockwise* direction. Secondly, the distance between two planets can never be wider than half the distance round the circle, which is 180°.

Here is a table of distances that can be employed when finding the arc of longitude between two planets:

Arc from ♈ 0° to end of ♈: 30°
Arc from ♈ 0° to end of ♉ : 60°
Arc from ♈ 0° to end of ♊ : 90°
Arc from ♈ 0° to end of ♋: 120°
Arc from ♈ 0° to end of ♌: 150°
Arc from ♈ 0° to end of ♍: 180°
Arc from ♈ 0° to end of ♎: 210°
Arc from ♈ 0° to end of ♏: 240°
Arc from ♈ 0° to end of ♐ : 270°
Arc from ♈ 0° to end of ♑: 300°
Arc from ♈ 0° to end of ♒: 330°

We will now start looking for aspects in Peter's chart (Fig. 7). What is the distance in arc of longitude between the Sun and Moon? The positioning of two planets, unless they are in *exactly* the same degree and minute, will always divide the ecliptic circle of 360° into two unequal arcs. It would be an extremely rare occasion when the two are equal, as the planets would be in *exactly* opposite degrees and minutes of the zodiac. When finding the distance between two bodies it is the *lesser* of the two arcs that is used.

It is clear from the positions of the Sun and Moon in Peter's chart that, measured anticlockwise, the arc from the Moon to the Sun is less than the arc from the Sun to the Moon. We therefore find what this lesser arc measures. To know this we subtract the position of the planet that is *behind* (in terms of an anticlockwise motion) from the position of the *leading* planet. If the position in degrees of the leading planet is *less* than that of the other planet, we add 360° to the position of the leading planet. Just how this can happen will be explained in our first example.

In Fig. 7 the Sun's position is shown as ♉ 16° 47′. From the tables of distances just given we find the measurement in *whole signs*, from Aries (♈), prior to the sign the Sun is in. To this amount we add the degrees and minutes of the Sun's position in Taurus (♉).

$$
\begin{aligned}
\text{One whole sign prior to ♉} &= 30° \ 00′ \\
\text{Sun's position in ♉} &= 16° \ 47′ \\
\hline
\text{Sun's longitude} &= 46° \ 47′
\end{aligned}
$$

We do the same with the Moon, noting from Fig. 7 that Moon is in ♐ 23° 51′.

$$
\begin{aligned}
\text{Eight whole signs (♈–♏) prior to ♐} &= 240° \ 00′ \\
\text{Moon's position in ♐} &= 23° \ 51′ \\
\hline
\text{Moon's longitude} &= 263° \ 51′
\end{aligned}
$$

To find the arc separating the Sun and Moon we must subtract the Moon's position from that of the "leading" body, the Sun. This is a case where 360° (12 whole signs) need to be *added* to the Sun's position.

$$
\begin{aligned}
\text{Sun's longitude} &= 46° \ 47′ \ (\text{add } 360°) = 406° \ 47′ \\
\text{Moon's longitude} &= 263° \ 51′ \phantom{(\text{add } 360°)} = 263° \ 51′ \\
\hline
\text{Difference} &= 142° \ 56′
\end{aligned}
$$

The arc of longitude separating the Sun and Moon is 142° 56′. Referring to the table of aspects and orbs on page 142 we will find this figure falls between two minor aspects, ⬜ or 135°, and ⊼ or 150°. An orb of only 2° is allowed for each aspect, which means that for the Sun and Moon to be in aspect their arc of difference would need to be, at the widest orbs, 137° or 148°. They do not form an aspect, and we make a small "dot" in the appropriate square.

To some students this method for finding possible aspects will seem rather "long winded", and I would say to these, go ahead with whichever other method you find quicker and as accurate. From my experience as tutor, however, I know that the method we have used for ☉ – ☽ will be most suitable for a great many other students. I will now give the calculations for a few further examples, using Peter's chart. Get out your pencil and paper and see if you can get the same results.

Are Sun and Uranus in aspect?

Sun is in   ♉ 16° 47′
Uranus is in   ♍ 15° 36′
Uranus is the leading planet.

Five whole signs prior to ♍	=	150° 00′
Uranus's position in ♍	=	15° 36′
Uranus's longitude	=	165° 36′

We have already calculated Sun's longitude: 46° 47′.

Uranus	=	165° 36′
Sun	=	46° 47′
Difference	=	118° 49′

Nearest aspect = △ (120°)
Margin of orb gives aspect limits as 112°–128°
Sun-Uranus are in △ aspect.

Are Moon and Jupiter in aspect?

Moon is in   ♐ 23° 51′
Jupiter is in ♋ 0° 26′

Moon is the leading body. We have calculated its longitude: 263° 51′.

Three whole signs prior to ♋	=	90° 00′
Jupiter's position in ♋	=	0° 26′
Jupiter's longitude	=	90° 26′

$$\begin{array}{lll} \text{Moon} & = & 263°\ 51' \\ \text{Jupiter} & = & 90°\ 26' \\ \hline \text{Difference} & = & 173°\ 25' \end{array}$$

Nearest aspect = ☍ (180°)
Margin of orb gives aspect limits as 172°
Moon-Jupiter are in ☍ aspect.

Are Venus and Saturn in aspect?

Venus is in ♈ 2° 56'
Saturn is in ♓ 26° 26'
Venus is the leading planet.

$$\begin{array}{lll} \text{No whole signs prior to ♈} & = & 0°\ 00' \\ \text{Venus's position in ♈} & = & 2°\ 56' \\ \hline \text{Venus's longitude} & = & 2°\ 56' \end{array}$$

$$\begin{array}{lll} \text{Eleven whole signs prior to ♓} & = & 330°\ 00' \\ \text{Saturn's position in ♓} & = & 26°\ 26' \\ \hline \text{Saturn's longitude} & = & 356°\ 26' \end{array}$$

$$\begin{array}{llll} \text{Venus} & = & 2°\ 56'\ (\text{add } 360°) & = & 362°\ 56' \\ \text{Saturn} & = & 356°\ 26' & = & 356°\ 26' \\ \hline & & \text{Difference} & = & 6°\ 30' \end{array}$$

Nearest aspect = ☌ (0°)
Margin of orb gives aspect limits as 8°
Venus-Saturn are in ☌ aspect.

Are Jupiter and Saturn in aspect?

Jupiter is in ♋ 0° 26'
Saturn is in ♓ 26° 26'
Jupiter is the leading planet.
We have already calculated Jupiter's longitude:
90° 26'

We have already calculated Saturn's longitude: 356° 26′

Jupiter	=	90° 26′ (add 360°)	=	450° 26′
Saturn	=	356° 26′	=	356° 26′
		Difference	=	94° 00′

Nearest aspect = □ (90°)
Margin of orb gives aspect limits as 82°–98°
Jupiter-Saturn are in □ aspect.

Now see if you can tabulate every aspect shown in Fig. 12 and also neatly draw in the aspect-lines as illustrated in Fig. 7.

Aspects to Ascendant and M.C.

The more accurate the known time of birth, the more important are any aspects formed by planets to the Ascendant and M.C. In Fig. 12 these aspects for Peter's chart are given. Aspect-lines are not generally drawn to the angles, but this is a matter of personal preference. Aspects are found in exactly the same way as for inter-planetary aspects.

Are Orbs Strictly Adhered to?

In the case of *major* aspects, when the 8° orb is exceeded by up to about 15′, these are instances when the aspect should be noted. This occurs in the case of ☽ □ ♅ in Peter's chart. In Fig. 12 the letter "w" is written against the square aspect symbol, reminding us that this is a *wide* aspect. It is not wise taking in too many wide aspects, since the theory is that the closer the aspect the more significant will it be within the chart-pattern. Therefore wide-orb aspects can only be weakened factors. The instances when wide-orbs (to 8° 15′) are worth noting is when one of the bodies is the Sun or Moon, or a planet conjunction an angle, or it is the Ascendant-Ruler, or is otherwise strongly-placed.

Mid-Points

An increasing interest is being shown in what are called *mid-points*. This refers to a point in the ecliptic midway between two planets, or between a planet and an angle. Aspects from other planets to these points can be formed, and transits and progressions across these points are considered very significant. Beginner-students need not bother with these for a while, but I would recommend their study to others. An example in Peter's chart: ♃–♅ mid-point is ♌ 8° 01′. This is arrived at by halving the distance between Jupiter and Uranus (75° 10′ ÷ 2 = 37° 35′) and adding this amount to Jupiter's position (♋ 0° 26′ + 37° 35′ = ♌ 8° 01′).

Parallel Aspect

The *parallel* is an aspect formed between two planets in terms of their relative positions in *declination*, as seen from the Earth. The *orb* allowed is 1½°. Each planet can be on the same side of the equator (both *north* declination, or both *south* declination), or on opposite sides (one planet *north*, the other *south*), for a parallel aspect to be formed, providing they are "within orb".

For example, in Peter's case Sun (16° 51′ N.) is parallel Mars (16° 10′ N.), and both Sun and Mars are parallel Neptune (16° 15′ S.). All parallels formed in Peter's chart, which you can check with reference to declinations listed on page 140, are:

Sun	parallel	Mars
Sun	parallel	Neptune
Sun	parallel	Ascendant
Mercury	parallel	M.C.
Mars	parallel	Neptune

Uranus   parallel M.C.
Pluto   parallel Ascendant

The symbol for the parallel is *P* or ‖.

Aspects to Nodes, Part of Fortune

Aspects can if wished be noted between planets and the Moon's nodes, or planets and the Part of Fortune. Except for the conjunction and opposition I have yet to find other aspects worth noting.

Exercises

The answers to these exercises can be found in Appendix VII.

What aspects are formed, strictly within orbs allowed on page 142, using the following longitude positions:

101. ⊙ in ♑ 18° 49′
    ☽ in ♐ 29° 50′
    ☿ in ♒ 7° 50′
    ♀ in ♒ 27° 52′
    ♂ in ♈ 22° 39′
    ♃ in ♎ 13° 56′
    ♄ in ♈ 16° 47′
    ♅ in ♑ 21° 02′
    ♆ in ♋ 17° 55′
    ♇ in ♊ 23° 23′
    ASC. in ♍ 25° 20′
    M.C. in ♊ 23° 15′.

What parallels are formed, strictly within 1½° orb, using the following declination positions:

102. ⊙ 17° 28′ S.
    ☽ 14° 10′ N.
    ☿ 16° 11′ S.
    ♀ 15° 22′ S.
    ♂ 8° 21′ N.

♃ 5° 58′ N.
♄ 16° 24′ S.
♅ 7° 18′ N.
♆ 9° 46′ N.
♇ 20° 14′ N.
ASC. 19° 06′ N.
M.C. 18° 02′ S.

17 *Classification of Chart Factors*

When the natal chart has been erected, and aspects between planets and angles noted, the astrologer likes to classify the planetary positions into various traditional categories. This enables him to see interesting features, and to note the most important factors in a systematic way.

The categories mentioned in this chapter are not necessarily used in their entirety by myself or any other astrologer. Indeed, some of these terms are considered old-fashioned and even obsolete, but they are listed because students will come upon these in astrological literature. For brevity, no attempt is made to explain the interpretational value of any factor, but each will be applied to our example case, Peter's chart (Fig. 7).

Ruler, or Sign-Ruler

Each planet is said to *rule* one or two signs, which means that the nature of the planet has "an affinity" with a particular sign or signs.

> ☉ rules ♌
> ☽ rules ♋
> ☿ rules ♊ ♍
> ♀ rules ♉ ♎
> ♂ rules ♈ ♏
> ♃ rules ♓ ♐
> ♄ rules ♒ ♑
> ♅ rules ♒
> ♆ rules ♓
> ♇ rules ♏

When we speak of *co-ruler* we are referring to one of two planets that rule the same sign. For instance, ♇ and ♂ are co-rulers of ♏; ♅ and ♄ are co-rulers of ♒; ♆ and ♃ are co-rulers of ♓.

Ruling Planet

The planet that rules the sign on the Ascendant. An older term was the *Significator*. Its importance can be seen by the fact that the Ascendant is also known as the *Ruling Sign*, meaning that both sign and ruling planet are dominating factors within the chart-pattern. In Peter's chart his Ascendant is Scorpio, therefore there are co-rulers of his chart, Pluto and Mars.

Sun-Ruler

The planet ruling the sign in which the Sun is placed. In Peter's chart the Sun is in Taurus (♉). Taurus is ruled by Venus, therefore Venus is Sun-Ruler.

Moon-Ruler

The planet ruling the sign in which the Moon is placed. In Peter's chart Moon is in Sagittarius, the sign ruled by Jupiter. Jupiter, therefore, is Moon-Ruler.

Own Sign

A planet is said to be "strengthened" when it is in its own sign, or the sign it rules. An old-fashioned expression was to speak of a planet being *at home* when in its own sign. In Peter's chart no planet is placed in its own sign.

Rising Planet

This is a classification applied to a planet that is rising at the eastern horizon or Ascendant at birth, and is within 8° orb of conjunction with this angle. This means that the planet can be within 8° of the Ascendant whether placed in the 12th house or 1st house. More than one planet within this orb may be considered as a group of equal significance as rising planets. In Peter's chart we see that Neptune is very close to the Ascendant, and is the rising planet.

Ruler's House

The house in which the Ruling Planet, or ruler of the Ascendant, is placed. Peter's chart has co-rulers, Pluto and Mars. Pluto's house is the 10th, Mars is the 6th, thus the affairs associated with both houses are considered of particular significance in the development of Peter's life and character.

Angular Planet

An angular planet in *Equal House* charting is one that is within 8° orb of conjunction at an *angle*. That is, if it is conjunction the Ascendant, the M.C., the Descendant, or the I.C., irrespective of the house it is in. This is a powerful position for a planet to be found in, and referring to Fig. 7 it will be seen that for Peter's chart the Sun, Mars, Neptune, Uranus, and Pluto are angular. The term is applied in rather a different way when using the *Placidus House System*. By this system a planet is said to be angular if it is in an *angular house* (1st, 4th, 7th, or 10th). Referring to Fig. 8 we find that Neptune, Saturn, Venus, Uranus and Pluto are "angular".

Succeedent Planets; Cadent Planets

These classifications are never applied to Equal House positioning of planets, only to quadrant systems such as Placidus. The *succeedent houses* follow or succeed the angular houses and are the 2nd, 5th, 8th, and 11th. Planets placed in any of these houses are listed on the chart-form as "succeedent", and in Fig. 8 we note that Moon, Mercury and Jupiter are of this classification. The *cadent houses* are the 3rd, 6th, 9th, and 12th by Placidus, and in Peter's case we find Sun and Mars, both in 6th, to be "cadent".

Triplicities, or Elements

The classification of the twelve signs into the four *elements*, Fire, Earth, Air, Water. The *Fire* triplicity are ♈ ♌ ♐, the *Earth* triplicity are ♉ ♍ ♑, the *Air* triplicity are ♊ ♎ ♒, the *Water* triplicity are ♋ ♏ ♓. Planets are classified under a particular triplicity according to the sign they are in. Peter's chart shows the following: Fire, ♀ ☿ (both in ♈) ☽ (♐); Earth, ☉ ♂ (♉) ♅ ♇ (♍); Air, none; Water, ♃ (♋) ♆ (♏) ♄ (♓).

Quadruplicities, or Qualities

The division of the twelve signs into three groups. These are the *Cardinal* signs ♈ ♋ ♎ ♑; the *Fixed* signs ♉ ♌ ♏ ♒; and the *Mutable* or *Common* signs ♊ ♍ ♐ ♓. A planet is classified under the particular group to which the sign it is in belongs. In Peter's case planets in *Cardinal* signs are ♀ ☿ (♈) ♃ (♋); those in *Fixed* signs are ☉ ♂ (♉) ♆ (♏); and in *Mutable* signs are ♅ ♇ (♍) ☽ (♐) ♄ (♓).

Positive and Negative

The twelve signs are divided into two categories, Positive and Negative, or in the older terminology, Masculine and Feminine. The *Positive* signs are Fire and Air, the *Negative* signs are Earth and Water. Add the number of planets in Fire and Air signs for the Positive category, and add the number in Earth and Water signs for the Negative category. In Peter's case we find there are *three* Positive and *seven* Negative.

Exalted

Traditionally a planet is said to be *exalted* or more "powerful" when in a sign of its *exaltation*. These exaltations are:

⊙ is exalted in ♈
☽ is exalted in ♉
☿ is exalted in ♍
♀ is exalted in ♓
♂ is exalted in ♑
♃ is exalted in ♋
♄ is exalted in ♎

In Peter's case we will find that only Jupiter, placed in ♋, is exalted.

Detriment; Fall

Another traditional idea, that a planet is weak or in the sign of its *detriment* when it is placed in the *opposite* sign to the sign it rules. Similarly, it is weak and in the sign of its *fall* when placed in the *opposite* sign to that of its exaltation. These are as follows:

	Detriment		*Fall*
⊙	♒		♎
☽	♑		♏
☿	♐	♓	♓
♀	♏	♈	♍
♂	♎	♉	♋
♃	♊	♍	♑
♄	♋	♌	♈
♅	♌		
♆	♍		
♇	♉		

In Peter's case, ♀ (in ♈) and ♂ (in ♉) would be entered under the *detriment* category on the chart-form, but no planet is in the sign of "its fall".

Mutual Reception

Another traditional, doubtful theory, that two planets are brought into relationship similar to a conjunction aspect if each is in a sign ruled by the other. There are two examples in Peter's chart. ☽ is in ♐ (ruled by ♃), and ♃ is in ♋ (ruled by ☽); ♀ is in ♈ (ruled by ♂), and ♂ is in ♉ (ruled by ♀).

Dispositor

A planet is said to be the *dispositor* of another when that other is in a sign ruled by this planet. The principle of a planet is affected by its dispositor. In Peter's chart, Venus is the dispositor of both Sun and Mars as these are in Taurus. Whilst Mars is in turn the dispositor of Venus and Mercury (both in Aries) and of Neptune in Scorpio. Each planet will have its dispositor unless it is in its own sign. As if there is not enough to cope with in astrology without adding this kind of complication!

Satellitium, or Stellium

A grouping of three or more planets, placing a significant emphasis on that portion of the chart. This does not occur in Peter's chart.

Aspect-Patterns

Marc Edmund Jones in *The Guide to Horoscope Interpretation* put forward an original classification of planetary groupings, in which certain types of these planetary-inter-relationships are shown to form distinct *patterns*. These are made especially clear by Equal House charting where aspect-lines are drawn in. Certain patterns emerge and we speak of these as *aspect-patterns*. Four of the main aspect-patterns will be described.

Grand Trine. A pattern formed by three trine aspects involving three or more planets. This does not occur in Peter's chart. But we can imagine how the triangle of aspect-lines would look if, apart from Saturn being trine Neptune, both planets were also trine to Jupiter.

Grand Cross. A pattern formed by two pairs of opposing planets involving four square aspects. This does not quite occur in Peter's chart. But we can imagine how the pattern of aspect-lines would appear, forming a cross within a square, if apart from Moon opposing Jupiter, Saturn also opposed Pluto; and apart from Moon square Pluto and Saturn, and Saturn square Jupiter, Jupiter were also square to Pluto.

T-Square. A pattern formed by two planets in opposition, each square to a third planet. This pattern occurs in Peter's chart. Moon opposes Jupiter, and each is in square aspect with Saturn.

See-Saw. The planets are split into two distinct and opposing groups, inevitably forming several opposition aspects.

Unaspected Planet

It is most important to make a special note of a planet that receives no aspect, and appears as a "disintegrated" factor in the chart.

Classification of Basic Drives and Conflicts

Few trained astrological-consultants from my experience are satisfied with the still commonly-used traditional terminology in their field of study. I have felt it necessary to inform the student of how to classify planets into the various traditional categories. But I would wish it to be known that I am in the process of reclassifying the entire structure of angles, signs, planets, aspect-patterns in terms of accepted modern psychological concepts.

Exercises

The answers to these exercises can be found in Appendix VII.

Enter the following data on to a chart-form:

ASC. ♌ 19°	♂ ♑ 10°
M.C. ♈ 3°	♃ ♐ 29°
☉ ♓ 26°	♄ ♓ 12°

☽ ♈ 9°   ♅ ♌ 21°
☿ ♓ 8°   ♆ ♉ 3°
♀ ♓ 13°   ♇ ♉ 22°

Then classify the factors into these categories:
103. Ruling planet.
104. Sun-Ruler.
105. Moon-Ruler.
106. Own sign.
107. Rising planet.
108. Ruler's house.
109. Angular planet by Equal House.
110. Fire, Earth, Air, Water Triplicities.
111. Cardinal, Fixed, Mutable Quadruplicities.
112. Positive and Negative.
113. Exalted, Detriment, and Fall.
114. Mutual reception.
115. Of which planet is the Sun the dispositor?
116. Do any planets form a satellitium?

18 *The Part of Fortune*

The *Part of Fortune*, or *Pars Fortunae*, or *Part of Destiny*, as it is variously called, is one of the thirty-two ancient "Arabic Parts". Its symbol is that of the Earth ⊕, and it is said to be associated with one's finances, material fortunes and possessions. I, like many other astrologers, have discarded it as not worth bothering with. It is, nevertheless, a symbolic point students will read about in astrological literature and for this reason each may like to test its validity for himself.

Its derivation is summed up by, "As the ☽ is to the ☉, so is the ⊕ to the Ascendant". Which means that the distance from the ☽ to the ☉ in a chart is equal to the distance from the ⊕ to the Ascendant.

To calculate ⊕:

(*a*) Add the longitude of the Ascendant to the longitude of the Moon.

(*b*) From this sum subtract the longitude of the Sun.

As an example we will calculate the Part of Fortune for Peter's chart.

	Sign	Degree	Mins
Ascendant = ♏ 20° 19′ (♏ =8th sign)	8	20	19
Moon = ♐ 23° 51′ (♐ =9th sign)	9	23	51
	18	14	10
Sun = ♉ 16° 47′ (♉ =2nd sign)	2	16	47
	15	27	23
When sign column exceeds *12*, sub-tract 12:	12		
	3	27	23

In the final answer, the *3* in the column headed "sign" refers to the *third* sign, which we know is Gemini (♊). Therefore the ⊕ for Peter's chart would be ♊ 27° 23'. We can check to see whether this is correct by comparing the distance between the Moon and Sun, with the distance between the ⊕ and the Ascendant. On page 146 we calculated the distance from the Moon to the Sun to be 142° 56'. The longitude in degrees and minutes from ♈ 0° to the ⊕ (♊ 27° 23') is two whole signs (60°) plus 27° 23' = 87° 23'. The distance from ♈ 0° to the Ascendant (♏ 20° 19') is seven whole signs (7 × 30° = 210°) plus 20° 19' = 230° 19'.

$$
\begin{array}{lll}
\text{Ascendant} & = & 230°\ 19' \\
\text{(subtract)}\ \oplus & = & \ \ 87°\ 23' \\
\hline
\oplus\ \text{to Asc.} & = & 142°\ 56'
\end{array}
$$

When, for the Sun, the number of *minutes* to be subtracted are greater than the number to be subtracted from, we "borrow" one whole degree of 60 minutes and add these to the number to be subtracted from. When, for the Sun, the number of *degrees* to be subtracted are greater than the number to be subtracted from, we "borrow" one whole sign of 30 degrees and add these to the number to be subtracted from. When, for the Sun, the number of *signs* to be subtracted are greater than the number to be subtracted from, we "borrow" 12 signs and add these to the number to be subtracted from. When, in the final calculated position for the Part of Fortune, the number in the "sign column" is *0* or *12*, either of these numbers will refer to the 12th sign, Pisces.

Exercises

Answers to these exercises can be found in Appendix VII.

Calculate the Part of Fortune, using the following data:

117. Asc. ♐ 10° 25'; ☽ ♊ 9° 12'; ☉ ♌ 22° 18'.
118. Asc. ♉ 1° 14'; ☽ ♎ 15° 30'; ☉ ♒ 20° 10'.

19 *Births Outside Great Britain*

The conversion of birth-time to G.M.T., and the calculation of the local sidereal time at birth, have been fully dealt with in Chapters 3–7. In this chapter two examples will be given in a straightforward manner where birth occurs in countries outside Great Britain and according to the Standard Time in operation. One birth will be in a country *east* of the Greenwich meridian, the other in a country *west* of the Greenwich meridian. Each will be typical of the method to be employed in converting birth-time to G.M.T. and for finding the local sidereal time at birth.

A birth occurs in Antwerp, Belgium (Lat. 51° 13′ N.; Long. 4° 24′ E.) on the 10th May 1966, at 8.15 p.m. Standard Time is 1 hour fast on G.M.T.

As Standard Time is 1 hour *fast* on G.M.T., because longitude is *east* of Greenwich, we *subtract* 1 hour from birth-time as given to convert to G.M.T.

		H.	*M.*	
Birth-time as given	=	8	15	p.m.
Subtract, as Long. E		1	00	
G.M.T.	=	7	15	p.m.

Referring to Fig. 3 we find the sidereal time at noon G.M.T. on the 10th May 1966, and proceed to find the local sidereal time at birth.

		H.	*M.*	*S.*
Sidereal time noon G.M.T.	=	3	11	21
Interval from noon (p.m. +)	=	7	15	00

Result	=	10	26	21
Acceleration on interval (p.m. +)	=		1	12
Sidereal time at Greenwich at birth	=	10	27	33
Longitude equivalent in time (E +)	=		17	36
Local sidereal time at birth	=	10	45	09

The second example is for a birth *west* of the Greenwich meridian.

A birth occurs in New York City, U.S.A. (Lat. 40° 45′ N.; Long. 74° 00′ W.) on the 28th May 1966, at 10.33 a.m. 1 hour Daylight Saving Time is in operation. New York uses Eastern Standard Time (E.S.T.) which is 5 hours slow on G.M.T.

As Daylight Saving Time is operating at birth we must *subtract* 1 hour from birth-time as given to convert this to E.S.T. Thus, as birth-time is 10.33 a.m., E.S.T. will be 9.33 a.m. The next step is to convert 9.33 a.m. E.S.T. into G.M.T., noting that E.S.T. is 5 hours *slow* on G.M.T.

		H.	*M.*	
Birth-time in E.S.T.	=	9	33	a.m.
Add, as Long. W.		5	00	
G.M.T. =		2	33	p.m.

Referring to Fig. 3 we find the sidereal time at noon G.M.T. on the 28th May 1966, and proceed to find the local sidereal time at birth.

		H.	*M.*	*S.*
Sidereal time noon G.M.T.	=	4	22	19
Interval from noon (p.m. +)	=	2	33	00
Result	=	6	55	19
Acceleration on interval (p.m. +)	=			25

Sidereal time at Greenwich at birth	=	6	55	44
Longitude equivalent in time (W –)	=	4	56	00
Local sidereal time at birth	=	1	59	44

Exercises

The answers to these exercises can be found in Appendix VII.

What is the local sidereal time at birth for the following cases:

119. Birth-data: 17th May 1966, in Cologne, Germany (Lat. 50° 56′ N.; 6° 57′ E.), at 5.55 a.m.
    Standard Time 1 hour fast on G.M.T.

120. Birth-data: 12th May 1966, in Los Angeles, U.S.A. (Lat. 34° 00′ N.; Long. 118° 10′ W.), at 1.15 a.m.
    1 hour Daylight Saving Time operating.
    Standard Time 8 hours slow on G.M.T.

20 *Southern Hemisphere Births*

The *Southern Hemisphere* is that half of the Earth's sphere between the equator and the south pole. Any place located in the Southern Hemisphere will have a *latitude* measured southwards from the equator.

When calculating the local sidereal time at birth, and the angles of the chart, for a birth occurring in the Southern Hemisphere there are two important adjustments to be made to the normal procedure for Northern Hemisphere births. These are:

1. 12 hours are *added* to the result of the addition or subtraction of longitude equivalent in time.
2. When referring to the latitude of birthplace in the *Tables of Houses for Northern Latitudes*, the signs as given for the Ascendant and M.C. (and for the other house cusps if using the Placidus System) must be *reversed*.

These two adjustments will be clearly explained in the following example.

A birth occurs: 20th May 1966
                2.35 p.m.
                Falkland Islands (51° 30′ S.; 59° 00′ W.)
                Standard Time is 4 hours slow on G.M.T.

The first step is to convert birth-time as given into G.M.T. Standard Time is 4 hours *slow* on, or *behind*, G.M.T., therefore we *add* 4 hours to the time given to convert this to G.M.T. This is simple: 2.35 p.m. plus 4 hours=6.35 p.m. G.M.T. We proceed in the normal way, as shown in previous chapters, to calculate the local sidereal time at birth, referring to Fig. 3 for the sidereal time at noon G.M.T. on the 20th May 1966.

		H.	M.	S.
Sidereal time noon G.M.T.	=	3	50	46
Interval from noon (p.m. +)	=	6	35	00
Result =		10	25	46
Acceleration on interval (p.m. +)	=		1	05
Sidereal time at Greenwich at birth	=	10	26	51
Longitude equivalent in time (W −)	=	3	56	00
Local sidereal time at birth, if birth were in Northern Hemisphere	=	6	30	51
ADD 12 hours, Southern Hem. birth	=	12	00	00
Local sidereal time at birth	=	18	30	51

We have made the first of the two adjustments because birthplace has a *south* latitude. Birthplace is 51° 30′ south, which is convenient, for we can turn to the *Tables of Houses for London* (51° 32′ N.) reproduced in Fig. 6. We want to find the signs and degrees on the angles of the chart corresponding to the *nearest* sidereal time in the tables to the local sidereal time at birth.

Local sidereal time at birth is *18H.30M.51S.* The nearest figures in the tables will be found to be *18H.30M. 30S.* We will read off the data for the M.C. and Ascendant as given in the tables:

$$\text{M.C.} \quad = \quad ♑ \ 7°$$
$$\text{Ascendant} \quad = \quad ♈ \ 18° \ 6′$$

These positions refer to the corresponding sidereal time if birth were in the Northern Hemisphere. So for our Southern Hemisphere birth there is the second adjustment to be made: the signs as given in the tables must be *reversed*. The correct data is therefore:

M.C.   =   ♋ 7°
Ascendant   =   ♎ 18° 6′

The signs on each of the house cusps will be reversed
also, but *the planets are not placed in opposite signs* to
those they appear in in the ephemeris. Beginners often
make this mistake.

Exercise

The answers to this exercise can be found in Appendix
VII.
A birth occurs in Auckland Islands, South Pacific Ocean
(51° 00′ S.; 166° 00′ E.), on the 5th May 1966, at 2.35
a.m.
Standard Time is 12 hours fast on G.M.T.
Using this data, and referring to Fig. 3 and Fig. 5 or
Fig. 6 as necessary, calculate the following:

121. Local sidereal time at birth.
122. Ascendant and M.C. corresponding to *nearest* sider-
     eal time in Tables of Houses.

APPENDIX I

Acceleration Tables

These tables give the corresponding sidereal time acceleration on each hour of mean time, and on each minute of
mean time. For a detailed explanation of the tables see
Chapter 6.

TABLE A

Mean Time Hours	Sidereal Time Acceleration M.	S.
0	0	0·0
1	0	9·9
2	0	19·7
3	0	29·6
4	0	39·4
5	0	49·3
6	0	59·1
7	1	9·0
8	1	18·9
9	1	28·7
10	1	38·6
11	1	48·4
12	1	58·3

TABLE B

Mean Time Mins.	Sidereal Time Acceleration Secs.	Mean Time Mins.	Sidereal Time Acceleration Secs.
0	0·0	2	0·3
1	0·2	3	0·5

Mean Time Mins.	Sidereal Time Acceleration Secs.	Mean Time Mins.	Sidereal Time Acceleration Secs.
4	0·7	32	5·3
5	0·8	33	5·4
6	1·0	34	5·6
7	1·1	35	5·7
8	1·3	36	5·9
9	1·5	37	6·1
10	1·6	38	6·2
11	1·8	39	6·4
12	2·0	40	6·6
13	2·1	41	6·7
14	2·3	42	6·9
15	2·5	43	7·1
16	2·6	44	7·2
17	2·8	45	7·4
18	3·0	46	7·6
19	3·1	47	7·7
20	3·3	48	7·9
21	3·4	49	8·0
22	3·6	50	8·2
23	3·8	51	8·4
24	4·0	52	8·5
25	4·1	53	8·7
26	4·3	54	8·9
27	4·4	55	9·0
28	4·6	56	9·2
29	4·8	57	9·4
30	4·9	58	9·5
31	5·1	59	9·7

Example:

What is the sidereal time acceleration on 5 hours
28 minutes of mean time?

5 hours mean time   = 49·3 seconds sidereal time
28 minutes mean time =   4·6 seconds sidereal time

5 hours 28 minutes   = $\overline{53\cdot9}$ seconds sidereal time
            Round off to 54 seconds

APPENDIX II

Conversion of Arc to Time

Tables for converting degrees and minutes of longitude into longitude equivalent in (mean solar) time. A detailed explanation of these tables is given in Chapter 7.

TABLE A

Arc °	Time H.	Time M.	Arc °	Time H.	Time M.	Arc °	Time H.	Time M.	Arc °	Time H.	Time M.
0	0	00	23	1	32	46	3	04	69	4	36
1	0	04	24	1	36	47	3	08	70	4	40
2	0	08	25	1	40	48	3	12	71	4	44
3	0	12	26	1	44	49	3	16	72	4	48
4	0	16	27	1	48	50	3	20	73	4	52
5	0	20	28	1	52	51	3	24	74	4	56
6	0	24	29	1	56	52	3	28	75	5	00
7	0	28	30	2	00	53	3	32	76	5	04
8	0	32	31	2	04	54	3	36	77	5	08
9	0	36	32	2	08	55	3	40	78	5	12
10	0	40	33	2	12	56	3	44	79	5	16
11	0	44	34	2	16	57	3	48	80	5	20
12	0	48	35	2	20	58	3	52	81	5	24
13	0	52	36	2	24	59	3	56	82	5	28
14	0	56	37	2	28	60	4	00	83	5	32
15	1	00	38	2	32	61	4	04	84	5	36
16	1	04	39	2	36	62	4	08	85	5	40
17	1	08	40	2	40	63	4	12	86	5	44
18	1	12	41	2	44	64	4	16	87	5	48
19	1	16	42	2	48	65	4	20	88	5	52
20	1	20	43	2	52	66	4	24	89	5	56
21	1	24	44	2	56	67	4	28	90	6	00
22	1	28	45	3	00	68	4	32	91	6	04

Arc °	Time H.	M.	Arc °	Time H.	M.	Arc °	Time H.	M.	Arc °	Time H.	M.
92	6	08	115	7	40	138	9	12	161	10	44
93	6	12	116	7	44	139	9	16	162	10	48
94	6	16	117	7	48	140	9	20	163	10	52
95	6	20	118	7	52	141	9	24	164	10	56
96	6	24	119	7	56	142	9	28	165	11	00
97	6	28	120	8	00	143	9	32	166	11	04
98	6	32	121	8	04	144	9	36	167	11	08
99	6	36	122	8	08	145	9	40	168	11	12
100	6	40	123	8	12	146	9	44	169	11	16
101	6	44	124	8	16	147	9	48	170	11	20
102	6	48	125	8	20	148	9	52	171	11	24
103	6	52	126	8	24	149	9	56	172	11	28
104	6	56	127	8	28	150	10	00	173	11	32
105	7	00	128	8	32	151	10	04	174	11	36
106	7	04	129	8	36	152	10	08	175	11	40
107	7	08	130	8	40	153	10	12	176	11	44
108	7	12	131	8	44	154	10	16	177	11	48
109	7	16	132	8	48	155	10	20	178	11	52
110	7	20	133	8	52	156	10	24	179	11	56
111	7	24	134	8	56	157	10	28	180	12	00
112	7	28	135	9	00	158	10	32			
113	7	32	136	9	04	159	10	36			
114	7	36	137	9	08	160	10	40			

TABLE B

Arc '	Time M.	S.	Arc '	Time M.	S.	Arc '	Time M.	S.	Arc '	Time M.	S.
0	0	00	6	0	24	12	0	48	18	1	12
1	0	04	7	0	28	13	0	52	19	1	16
2	0	08	8	0	32	14	0	56	20	1	20
3	0	12	9	0	36	15	1	00	21	1	24
4	0	16	10	0	40	16	1	04	22	1	28
5	0	20	11	0	44	17	1	08	23	1	32

Arc	Time		Arc	Time		Arc	Time		Arc	Time	
'	M.	S.	'	M.	S.	'	M.	S.	'	M.	S.
24	1	36	33	2	12	42	2	48	51	3	24
25	1	40	34	2	16	43	2	52	52	3	28
26	1	44	35	2	20	44	2	56	53	3	32
27	1	48	36	2	24	45	3	00	54	3	36
28	1	52	37	2	28	46	3	04	55	3	40
29	1	56	38	2	32	47	3	08	56	3	44
30	2	00	39	2	36	48	3	12	57	3	48
31	2	04	40	2	40	49	3	16	58	3	52
32	2	08	41	2	44	50	3	20	59	3	56

Example:

The longitude of Moscow is 37° 35' E.

What is the required Longitude Equivalent in Time?

From *Table A*: 37° arc of longitude   =   2*H*.28*M*.

From *Table B*: 35' arc of longitude   =   2*M*.20*S*.

37° 35' =   2*H*.30*M*.20*S*.

APPENDIX III

Recommended Requirements

Raphael's Ephemeris (W. Foulsham & Co. Ltd., Yeovil Road, Slough, Bucks, England).

An annual publication, from 1860 to date, giving the longitudes of the planets, and sidereal time, for noon at Greenwich on each day of the year. Declinations, daily motions of the planets, complete aspects for the entire year, and many more detailed astronomical phenomena.

Raphael's Tables of Houses for Northern Latitudes (W. Foulsham & Co. Ltd., Yeovil Road, Slough, Bucks, England).

Covering Northern Hemisphere latitudes 2° to 50°, also 59° 56', which can be converted for the corresponding latitudes in the Southern Hemisphere.

Raphael's Tables of Houses for Great Britain (W. Foulsham & Co. Ltd., Yeovil Road, Slough, Bucks, England).

Covering 18 different Northern Hemisphere latitudes between 50° 22' and 59°, which are serviceable not only for the whole of Great Britain but for all places in the mid-latitudes of Europe, Asia, and North America. These tables can also be converted for the corresponding latitudes in the Southern Hemisphere.

The Influence of the Planet Pluto, by Elbert Benjamine (The Aries Press, 1035 West Lake Street, Chicago 7, Illinois, U.S.A.).

Contains an *ephemeris* of Pluto from 1840–1939, and a much abbreviated ephemeris for 1940–1960.

Fowler's Ephemeris 1955–1959 (L. N. Fowler & Co. Ltd., 15 New Bridge Street, London, E.C.4, England).

Longitudes, declinations, and latitudes of the Sun, Moon, and planets (including Pluto), and sidereal time, for noon at Greenwich on each day of the year, and covering five years.

Fowler's Ephemeris 1960–1964 (L. N. Fowler & Co. Ltd., 15 New Bridge Street, London, E.C.4, England).
Similar contents to the above ephemeris.

Fowler's Ephemeris 1965–1969 (L. N. Fowler & Co. Ltd., 15 New Bridge Street, London, E.C.4, England).
Similar contents to the above ephemeris.

Die Deutsche Ephemeride, Vol. 1 (1850–1889).
Die Deutsche Ephemeride, Vol. 2 (1890–1930).
Die Deutsche Ephemeride, Vol. 3 (1931–1950).
Die Deutsche Ephemeride, Vol. 4 (1951–1960).
Die Deutsche Ephemeride, Vol. 5 (1961–1970).
(Each volume published by Otto Wilhelm Barth-Verlag, Weilheim/Obb., West Germany). No knowledge of German required. Longitudes and declinations of the Sun and Moon, longitudes of the planets (not Pluto), and sidereal time, for each day. Declinations of the planets for every third day. Note, however, that positions given in Vols. 1 and 2 are for noon G.M.T.; Vols. 3, 4 and 5 are for midnight G.M.T. at the beginning of the day. See Appendix IV for how to use the "midnight ephemeris".

The Astrologer's Astronomical Handbook, by Jeff Mayo, D.F.Astrol.S. (L. N. Fowler & Co. Ltd., 15 New Bridge Street, London, E.C.4, England).
The Astrologer's Handbook Series No. 1. The standard reference work on astronomical factors which form the basis of astrological charting. 21 illustrations. Time-systems explained. Full Index.

How to Read the Ephemeris, by Jeff Mayo, D.F. Astrol.S. (L. N. Fowler & Co. Ltd., 15 New Bridge Street, London, E.C.4, England).
The Astrologer's Handbook Series No. 2. An essential

reference book for the beginner. *Raphael's Ephemeris* is "dissected" and explained in the fullest detail. 11 whole page reproductions. Index.

Time Changes in the U.S.A., by Doris Chase Doane. (The Church of Light, P.O. Box 1525, Los Angeles, California 90053, U.S.A.).

The most comprehensive book available on the complex systems of Standard Time, Daylight Saving Time, and War Time, in the U.S.A. Complete dates and variations in time systems dealt with State by State. A *vital* reference book for all who calculate charts for births in the U.S.A.

Gazetteer. No particular gazetteer is recommended here because prices vary considerably, and sometimes there is difficulty in obtaining titles locally. Students should make enquiries of local suppliers.

Calculation-Forms (Designed by Margaret Hone, D.F. Astrol.S.).

Form A. Summarized instructions for calculation of zodiacal positions of the planets for given time, with spaces to enter working for a chart.

Form B. Summarized instructions for calculation for Local Sidereal Time for given time in order to obtain Ascendant and Midheaven, with spaces to enter working for a chart.

Chart-Forms (Designed by Margaret Hone, D.F.Astrol.S.).

No. 1. The "Ecliptic" Chart. Spaces for entering calculations and other details, as well as the basic chart showing the circle of 360°—convenient for entering planets in correct positions.

No. 2. The "Houses" Chart. Spaces for entering calculations and other details, as well as the basic chart with house cusps. This is the recommended chart-form for students, whichever house system is used.

Enlarged Logarithm Card (Designed by Margaret Hone, D.F.Astrol.S.).

Stencil (Designed by Margaret Hone, D.F.Astrol.S.).
For quick insertion of house-lines on Ecliptic Chart.

Reference books and chart-forms dealing with astro-logical progressions and transits have not been listed, as it is hoped to include a title in The Astrologer's Handbook Series devoted entirely to this side of calculations and theory.

Standard Times; Daylight Saving or Summer Times.

Unfortunately there is no publication available that lists the complete variations in time-systems throughout the world since each country adopted synchronized time. Current details are given in *The Nautical Almanac* (H.M. Stationery Office), and in *Whitaker's Almanack*, both published annually. A full list of Standard Times (for 1952) appear in *The Modern Textbook of Astrology*, by Margaret Hone (L. N. Fowler & Co. Ltd.), and a list (for 1960) is given in *Teach Yourself Astrology*, by Jeff Mayo (The English Universities Press Ltd., 102 Newgate Street, London, E.C.1). The complete list of Summer Times in Great Britain from 1916–1967 are given in *How to Read the Ephemeris*, by Jeff Mayo (L. N. Fowler & Co. Ltd.). Another useful book dealing with time variations is *World Time Differences*, com-piled by Edward W. Whitman. In the case of important charts, and when in doubt about the time system in operation, the student is advised to write to the Embassy of the country concerned, the address of which can usually be obtained from reference sources in the Public Library.

Current prices of recommended items are not given as these can change. It is suggested that the student writes to the publishers of this book for details and Astrological

Catalogue, and from whom all the recommended items can be purchased:

L. N. Fowler & Co. Ltd.
15 New Bridge Street
London, E.C.4.
England

How to Use the Midnight Ephemeris

The student must be careful when buying an ephemeris other than *Raphael's*, to make sure that the sidereal time and planets' positions are calculated for *noon G.M.T. at Greenwich*. Some ephemerides are calculated for *midnight*. An instance is *Die Deutsche Ephemeride*, Vols. 3–5. These are excellent ephemerides, but if you are used to calculating birth-charts from an ephemeris giving *noon* positions of the planets, and for sidereal time, you may be rather confused as to how to apply *midnight* positions.

The adjustment to make is quite simple. As an example we will refer to *Die Deutsche Ephemeride*, Vol. 5. This volume covers the years 1961–1970 inclusive, and the planets' positions, and sidereal time, are calculated to *midnight at the beginning of each day*. As we have been using the pages for *May 1966* from *Raphael's Ephemeris*, it would be convenient to choose a couple of dates in that month from the German ephemeris, so that our results can be compared with the same dates in Fig. 3.

The idea is to convert the midnight positions into noon positions so that the normal procedure for chart calculation can be followed. As positions are given for midnight at the *beginning* of the day, we simply find the *midway positions* between those at the *beginning* of the day and those at the *end* of the day (which would be those given for the beginning of the following day).

Example: Referring to *Die Deutsche Ephemeride*, Vol. 5, what is the Sun's *noon* position in longitude on the 7th May 1966?

Step 1. Find the Sun's position at midnight beginning of the 7th May. It is ♉ 15° 59′ 15″.

Step 2. Find the Sun's position at midnight the following day, 8th May (which is, of course, the Sun's position at midnight at the *end* of the 7th). It is ♉ 16° 57′ 17″.

Step 3. Find the Sun's daily motion, by subtracting its position on the 7th from its position on the 8th.

Sun, at midnight (0.00 a.m.) 8th May = ♉ 16° 57′ 17″
Sun, at midnight (0.00 a.m.) 7th May = ♉ 15° 59′ 15″
                                          ─────────────
          Sun's daily motion =   58′ 02″

Step 4. Divide the Sun's daily motion by 2, and add the result to its position at 0.00 a.m. on 7th May. This will give the Sun's position in longitude at noon on the 7th May 1966. Daily motion was found to be 58′ 02″. Divided by 2 = 29′ 01″.

Sun, at midnight (0.00 a.m.) 7th May = ♉ 15° 59′ 15″
        Add half of daily motion   =   29′ 01″
                                          ─────────────
Sun's position noon G.M.T. 7th May = ♉ 16° 28′ 16″

If we refer to Fig. 3, the Sun's position in longitude at noon G.M.T. on the 7th May 1966 will be seen to be exactly the same as the above reading.

In the case of the Moon, whose daily motion is so much greater than the other bodies, there is often a slight discrepancy between the noon position calculated from the German ephemeris using the above method, and the corresponding date for noon in *Raphael's Ephemeris*. This is due to the Moon's rate of motion varying each hour, and for practical purposes the discrepancy is nothing to worry about.

The *sidereal time* as given for midnight (0.00 a.m. G.M.T.) in the German ephemeris must also be converted to its noon reading, as follows:

1. Find the sidereal time at midnight (0.00 a.m.) on given date; and the sidereal time at midnight (0.00 a.m.) for the following day. Subtract the former from the latter, and divide the result by 2.
2. Add the result of (1) to the sidereal time at midnight (0.00 a.m.) on given date.
3. Subtract 12 hours from the result of (2). The answer will be sidereal time at noon G.M.T. on given date.

Example: what is the sidereal time at noon G.M.T. 7th May 1966, using *Die Deutsche Ephemeride*, Vol. 5?

Step 1.
| Sidereal time midnight 8th May | = | 15H.01M.29S. |
| Sidereal time midnight 7th May | = | 14H.57M.33S. |

| | Difference | = | 3M.56S. |

Divide difference by 2, gives 1M.58S.

Step 2.
| Sidereal time at midnight 7th May | = | 14H.57M.33S. |
| Add result of Step 1 | = | 1M.58S. |

| | Result | = | 14H.59M.31S. |

| Step 3. | | 14H.59M.31S. |
| Subtract | | 12H.00M.00S. |

| | | 2H.59M.31S. |

Referring to Fig. 3, we find that *Raphael's Ephemeris* confirms that sidereal time at noon G.M.T. on the 7th May 1966 is 2H.59M.31S.

APPENDIX V

When Time of Birth is Unknown

Many people do not know their time of birth, others have only a vague idea of when it may have occurred. Particularly in the latter case there are various methods of *rectification*, by which a *speculative time* is arrived at, as is indicated on pages 17–18.

When the time of birth is unknown, and perhaps it is difficult even to choose a possible time, or the case is not of sufficient importance to warrant spending time on rectification, or because of lack of information about the person it would be impossible to attempt to speculate on the possible Ascendant, there are three types of chart the astrologer can choose from to set up.

1. The *flat* chart.
2. The *approximate sunrise* chart, or *solarscope*.
3. The *true sunrise* chart.

To erect a flat chart is as simple as A.B.C. The first sign of the zodiac, Aries, is placed on the first house cusp (♈ 0°); the second sign, Taurus, is placed on the second house cusp (♉ 0°); the third sign, Gemini, is placed on the third house cusp (♊ 0°); and so on, right round the houses of the chart, until the twelfth sign, Pisces, is placed on the twelfth house cusp (♓ 0°). Since the time of birth is not known, the planets are entered in the chart according to their noon position given in the ephemeris for the birth-date. It does not matter in which part of the world birth occurred, since no calculations involving birthplace co-ordinates are made. Naturally only generalized indications of character may be given through a *flat* chart.

The *approximate sunrise* chart, or *solarscope* as it is often called in America, is what is erected when the astrologer places the *Sun* exactly on the first house cusp. It is only an *approximate* sunrise chart because it is the Sun's position as given in the ephemeris for *noon* on birth-date that is used. Likewise, the planets are also entered in this chart according to their noon positions. The houses are of equal size (30°), because the same degree and minute occupied by the Sun at noon is entered against each house cusp, only the *sign* being different. Thus, if Sun's noon position were ♊ 12° 25′, the longitude on the first house cusp would be ♊ 12° 25′. The following sign would be on the second house cusp, ♋ 12° 25′; on the third house cusp would be ♌ 12° 25′, and so on round the chart. As with the flat chart, only generalized indications of character may be given.

The *true sunrise* chart is a chart calculated in the normal way, as when the time of birth is known, using the *true* time of sunrise for the latitude of the birthplace, as though it were the actual moment of birth. The planets' positions are also calculated to this elected time. Any method of house division may be used as desired. The local mean time of sunrise for given latitudes for dates throughout the year are given annually in *Raphael's Ephemerides*, and the method by which sunrise can be calculated for any date and any latitude with the use of the data given in the ephemeris is explained in *How to Read the Ephemeris*, Chapter 21. Again it must be stressed that only generalized indications of character may be given through this type of chart, as with the other two types explained.

Births in Local Mean Time

The occasion may arise when the student will want to
calculate a chart for a birth given in *Local Mean Time*,
which would be the time-system used before the country
of birth adopted Standard Time. It is reasonable to
assume that any such Local Mean Time for birth is
unlikely to be the true birth time, since there would have
been no accurate method of synchronizing watches and
clocks in different localities or even within the same
locality. Therefore one need not be too fastidious regarding calculating the angles of the chart to exact minutes
of longitude.

In the British Isles on the 1st October 1880 British
Standard Time (G.M.T.) was adopted. Prior to this date
Local Mean Time was in operation. Of course a particular
snag one may encounter is not being able to obtain the
ephemeris for an earlier year in the 19th century. However,
as an example this could be the procedure for calculating
the local sidereal time at birth for a birth given as:

> 10th June 1864
> 5.20 p.m. Local Mean Time (L.M.T.)
> Halifax, England (53° 43' N.; 1° 51' W.)

As the ephemeris we would be using is based on the
Local Mean Time for London (Greenwich), and birth-
time is given in Local Mean Time for Halifax, the first
step is to convert the birthplace L.M.T. into the corresponding Greenwich L.M.T. This is similar to the step
we know as *Longitude Equivalent in Time*, except that:

(*a*) When longitude is *west* of Greenwich, the longitude

equivalent in time is *added* to L.M.T. for birthplace to convert to Greenwich L.M.T.

(*b*) When longitude is *east* of Greenwich, the longitude equivalent in time is *subtracted* from L.M.T. for birthplace to convert to Greenwich L.M.T.

Referring to the tables in Appendix II we will find that the longitude for Halifax (1° 51′)=7 minutes 24 seconds of time. As Halifax is *west* of Greenwich, 7M.24S. has to be *added* (Rule (*a*) above) to birth-time (5.20 p.m.) to give Greenwich L.M.T.

H.	M.	S.	
5	20	00	p.m.
	7	24	
5	27	24	p.m. (Greenwich L.M.T.)

We then proceed as follows:

		H.	M.	S.
Sidereal time noon Greenwich	=	5	16	22
Interval from noon (p.m. +)	=	5	27	24
Result	=	10	43	46
Acceleration on interval (p.m. +)	=			54
Sidereal time at Greenwich at birth	=	10	44	40
Longitude equivalent in time (W –)	=		7	24
Local sidereal time at birth	=	10	37	16

I wonder, have you realized that these calculations simply produce a local sidereal time for a 5.20 p.m. L.M.T. Halifax birth, the same as for a 5.20 p.m. L.M.T. London birth? *Sidereal time at noon* for London is the same *for noon* at Halifax. *The only calculation to find local sidereal time for the above Halifax birth would be to add 5 hours 20 minutes and 53 seconds acceleration to the noon sidereal time. No longitude adjustment is needed.*

Exercise Answers

Here are the answers to the exercises set at the end of many of the chapters.

1. 3.23 p.m. G.M.T., 11th July 1938.
2. 11.14 a.m. G.M.T., 28th April 1945.
3. 11.37 p.m. G.M.T., 31st May 1957.
4. 5.00 p.m. G.M.T., 22nd March 1965.
5. 3.35 a.m. G.M.T., 23rd March 1965.
6. 7.22 a.m. G.M.T., 10th June 1966.
7. 5.40 p.m. G.M.T., 19th May 1960.
8. 2H.35M. 52S.
9. 2H.39M.48S.
10. 3H.11M.21S.
11. 3H.58M.39S.
12. 2H.35M.52S.
13. 3H.03M.28S.
14. 2H.35M.52S.
15. 4H.22M.19S.
16. 2H.35M.52S.
17. 3H.31M.03S.
18. 0H.05M.
19. 11H.55M.
20. 3H.43M.
21. 8H.17M.
22. 6H.00M.
23. 6H.00M.
24. 9H.27M.
25. 2H.33M.
26. 0H.00M.
27. 12H.00M.

28. 5H.27M.31S.
29. 17H.27M.31S.
30. 14H.46M.31S.
31. 2H.46M.31S.
32. 0H.00M.31S.
33. 28H.03M.15S.
34. 8H.52M.15S.
35. 30H.15M.15S.
36. 25H.22M.15S.
37. 0M.24S.
38. 0M.06S.
39. 1M.10S.
40. 1M.42S.
41. 2M.00S.
42. 1M.32S.
43. 1M.20S.
44. 1M.07S.
45. 0M.59S.
46. 0M.17S.
47. 0M.23·3S. 0M.23S.
48. 0M.06·2S. 0M.06S.
49. 1M.09·0S. 1M.09S.
50. 1M.40·2S. 1M.40S.
51. 1M.58·1S. 1M.58S.
52. 1M.30·7S. 1M.31S.
53. 1M.19·2S. 1M.19S.
54. 1M. 06·3S. 1M.06S.
55. 0M.58·3S. 0M. 58S.
56. 0M.16·6S. 0M.17S.
57. 22H.07M.27S.
58. 9H.21M.32S.
59. 5H.09M.32S.
60. 1H.39M.38S.
61. (a) 6H.03M.52S. (b) 16H.37M.36S.
62. (a) 11H.52M.00S. (b) 10H.33M.28S.
63. (a) 0H.00M.44S. (b) 22H.40M.44S.

64. (*a*) 8H.09M.20S.   (*b*) 14H.32M.08S.
65. (*a*) 0H.35M.48S.   (*b*) 23H.17M.16S.
66. ASC.–DESC. axis; M.C.–I.C. axis.
67. 11H.15M.52S.
    Asc. ♏ 25° 27′; M.C. ♍ 18°.
68. 21H.21M.47S.
    Asc. ♊ 23° 52′; M.C. ♒ 18°.
69 18H.00M.00S.
    Asc. ♈ 0° 00′; M.C. ♑ 0°.
70. 12H.00M.00S.
    Asc. ♐ 3° 23′; M.C. ♎ 0°.
71. 00H.00M.00S.
    Asc. ♋ 26° 36′; M.C. ♈ 0°.
72. 00H.00M.00S.
    Asc. ♋ 26° 36′; M.C. ♈ 0°.

73. Cusp 1 = ♍ 26° 09′
    Cusp 2 = ♎ 20°
    Cusp 3 = ♏ 19°
    Cusp 4 = ♐ 25°
    Cusp 5 = ♒ 1°
    Cusp 6 = ♓ 2°
    Cusp 7 = ♓ 26° 09′
    Cusp 8 = ♈ 20°
    Cusp 9 = ♉ 19°
    Cusp 10 = ♊ 25°
    Cusp 11 = ♌ 1°
    Cusp 12 = ♍ 2°
    ♑ intercepted in 4th
    ♋ intercepted in 10th.

74. Cusp 1 = ♐ 17° 29′
    Cusp 2 = ♑ 28°
    Cusp 3 = ♓ 15°
    Cusp 4 = ♈ 20°
    Cusp 5 = ♉ 14°
    Cusp 6 = ♊ 2°
    Cusp 7 = ♊ 17° 29′

Cusp 8 = ♋ 28°
Cusp 9 = ♍ 15°
Cusp 10 = ♎ 20°
Cusp 11 = ♏ 14°
Cusp 12 = ♐ 2°
♒ intercepted in 2nd
♌ intercepted in 8th.

75. Cusp 1 = ♋ 29° 55′
    Cusp 2 = ♌ 16°
    Cusp 3 = ♍ 7°
    Cusp 4 = ♎ 5°
    Cusp 5 = ♏ 14°
    Cusp 6 = ♐ 26°
    Cusp 7 = ♑ 29° 55′
    Cusp 8 = ♒ 16°
    Cusp 9 = ♓ 7°
    Cusp 10 = ♈ 5°
    Cusp 11 = ♉ 14°
    Cusp 12 = ♊ 26°
    No intercepted signs.

76. Exact Asc. = ♓ 8° 16′   I = 221 mins.
    Exact M.C. = ♐ 24°08′   J = 31 mins.
    A = 262 secs.   K = ♓ 7° 08′
    B = 37 secs.   L = 58 mins.
    C = 60 mins.   M = 20 mins.
    D =   8 mins.   N = 104 mins.
    E = ♐ 24° 08′   O = 35·86 mins.
    F = 206 mins.   (round off to 36
    G = 29 mins.   mins.)
    H = ♓ 8° 52′   P = ♓ 8° 16′.

77. 0·8487

78. 0·3388

79. 1·3875

80. 0·7302

81. 0·1984

82. 0·4508

83. 0° 07′

84. 11° 37′

85. 2° 27′

86. 1° 34′

87. (a) 1·1202 (b) 1° 49′

88. (a) 1·7876 (b) 0° 23′

89. (a) 0·5452 (b) 6° 50′

90. (a) 0·7896 (b) 3° 54′

91.			92.		
☉	♉	14° 58′	☉	♉	26° 39′
☽	♏	28° 41′	☽	♈	28° 45′
☿	♈	23° 48′	☿	♉	15° 55′
♀	♈	0° 50′	♀	♈	14° 23′
♂	♉	13° 25′	♂	♉	22° 13′
♃	♋	0° 04′	♃	♋	2° 28′
♄	♓	26° 15′	♄	♓	27° 20′
♅	♍	15° 38′ R.	♅	♍	15° 30′ R.
♆	♏	20° 59′ R.	♆	♏	20° 39′ R.
♇	♍	15° 56′ R.	♇	♍	15° 50′ R.
☊	♉	26° 02′	☊	♉	25° 23′
☋	♏	26° 02′	☋	♏	25° 23′

93. 1° 32′ N.
94. 23° 21′ S.
95. 23° 04′ N.
96. 1° 07′ S.
97. ☉ 17° 23′ N.; ♀ 0° 36′ N.; ♂ 16° 35′ N.
98. ☉ 17° 58′ N.; ♀ 1° 32′ N.; ♂ 17° 05′ N.
99. ☉ 19° 57′ N.; ♀ 4° 58′ N.; ♂ 18° 47′ N.
100. ☉ 21° 14′ N.; ♀ 7° 43′ N.; ♂ 20° 00′ N.
101. ☉ □ ♂ ♃ ♄   ♀ △ ♇ M.C.
    ☉ ☌ ♅   ♂ ☌ ♄
    ☉ ☍ ♆   ♂ □ ♅ ♆
    ☉ △ Asc.   ♂ ✶ ♇ M.C.
    ☽ ✶ ♀   ♃ ☍ ♄
    ☽ △ ♂   ♃ □ ♅ ♆
    ☽ ☍ ♇ M.C.   ♄ □ ♅ ♆
    ☽ □ Asc.   ♅ ☍ ♆
    ☿ △ ♃   ♅ △ Asc.
    ☿ ⊡ ♇ M.C.   ♇ □ Asc.
    ♀ ✶ ♂   ♇ ☌ M.C.
    ♀ ⊡ ♃
102. ☉ P ☿ ♄ M.C.   ♂ P ♅ ♆
    ☽ P ♀   ♃ P ♅
    ☿ P ♀ ♄   ♇ P Asc.
    ♀ P ♄
103. ☉
104. ♆ ♃
105. ♂
106. ♃
107. ♅
108. 8th.
109. ♅ ☽ ☉
110. F. ☽ ♅ ♃
    E. ♆ ♇ ♂
    A. Nil
    W. ☿ ♄ ♀ ☉
111. C. ☽ ♂

F. ♆ ♇ ♅

M. ♃ ☿ ♄ ♀ ☉

112. Pos: 3; Neg: 7.

113. Exalted: ♂ ♀

Detriment: ♇ ☿ ♅

Fall: ☿

114. ♀ – ♆

115. ♅

116. ♀ ♄ ☿ (☉)

117. ⊕ ♍ 27° 19′.

118. ⊕ ♐ 26° 34′.

119. 21H.00M.35S.

120. 15H.40M.57S.

121. 4H.27M.06S.

122. Asc. ♓ 14° 00′.

M.C. ♐ 9° 00′.

Index